THE
HEDGE TREE
HANDBOOK

THE TREE COUNCIL

FOREWORD

Britain's hedge trees are in decline. Without concerted effort they will continue to be under threat.

Hedges and hedge trees have always played a variety of important roles in British history: as vital habitats for a multitude of wildlife; as sources of food, fuel and timber; as boundary markers; as shelter for livestock; and not least, of course, as beautiful and enjoyable features of our countryside.

Since the late 18th century, however, the abundance of hedge trees has dramatically declined. Periodic changes in farming techniques and agricultural needs, increased use of machinery, hedge removal, Dutch elm disease, neglect and lack of replacement have all taken their toll of the hedge tree population.

This book explains the value of hedge trees, explores their fascinating history and points the way to halting their decline as well as to the action needed now to establish the hedge trees of the future.

The Tree Council hopes that in these pages you will find much to interest you and to increase your awareness of the importance of hedges and hedge trees – not only to the beauty of the British landscape but especially to its biodiversity, to which they make a vital contribution.

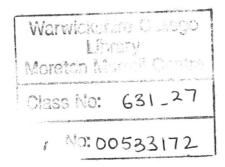

CONTENTS

HEDGE TREES MATTER

The wildlife and landscape significance of trees growing in British hedges is immense. They are an important part of our heritage, a vital feature of our national treescape and a rare part of Europe's ecology. Over the last 30 years, however, several million hedge trees have been lost from our countryside. Nearly a third of those that remain are over a century old.

Hedge trees, once valued as an important part of a farm system, have dramatically declined in number since the late 18th century through hedge removal, Dutch elm disease and many other factors. Changes in agricultural practices also mean that there are very few young trees to take their place.

With urgent action needed to establish new hedge trees and prevent greater changes to the landscape and its biodiversity, the Tree Council, in partnership with National Grid Transco, is leading the Hedge Tree Campaign to increase awareness of why hedge trees matter and to halt their decline.

To champion the cause of hedge trees, the Tree Council is enlisting the support of its 7,500 volunteer Tree Wardens throughout the UK, its member organisations, local authorities and other supporters including farmers, landowners and contractors who are key to the success of the campaign. As many members of the general public as possible are also being encourage to become involved.

The Hedge Tree Campaign aims to:

- increase awareness that 'Hedge Trees Matter' – for biodiversity, farming, landscape, cultural and archaeological reasons

- halt the decline of hedgerow trees and increase their number – by planting new ones and saving those that exist, thus encouraging saplings to grow into tomorrow's mature and eventually ancient trees

- manage and maintain ancient trees in hedges – as they have great intrinsic and ecological value.

The campaign will help to achieve the targets of local and national Biodiversity Action Plans (BAPs). It will also help to maintain the overall number of individual hedge trees, estimated to be 1.8 million in Great Britain, through ensuring a balanced age structure. One way to ensure that there are hedge trees in the future is to mark newly-planted trees or existing saplings with easy-to-see tags. This will help whoever cuts the hedge to avoid the tagged young trees, allowing them to grow to maturity.

This book outlines the importance, history and good management of hedge trees and shows what can be done to grow new ones. The Tree Council therefore hopes that this book will encourage people to look at hedge trees with new enthusiasm, enabling them to play a role in protecting this vital part of Britain's national heritage.

8

THE VALUE OF HEDGES AND HEDGE TREES

A hedge is a form of 'topiary': that is, the management of trees and shrubs into a particular shape and form, for a particular purpose. The woody trees which make up hedges – hawthorn, blackthorn, hazel and many other species – are kept short as a result of management.

The natural tendency of hedge trees is to grow tall but they are malleable and tolerant of pruning. By simply not cutting a section of hedge if the required species are present (or by deliberate planting if necessary), a mature tree can be grown in a hedge line without great effort.

The accompanying illustration shows the variety of valuable functions that well managed hedges and hedge trees have in the landscape.

1 A feature to enhance a roadside or house

2 A link between other elements in the landscape such as woods, which can be valuable for wildlife

3 Food and medicines including herbs in hedge bottoms

4 Cover for game species

5 Timber and firewood

6 Jumps for horse riding

To quote Philip Miller (1741) [1]:

"Hedges afford the diligent husbandman plenty of fuel, as also plough boot, cart boot and where they are carefully planted and preserved, furnish him with timber and mast for his swine. Or where the hedge-rows are planted with fruit trees, there will be a plentiful supply of fruits for cider, perry etc., which in most parts of England are of no small advantage to the husbandman."

Throughout history, land managers saw the hedge and its trees as a way of supplementing their much needed wood supplies, of providing winter fodder for stock and of producing foodstuffs from the boundaries of their land. These multi-purpose boundaries were therefore considered of great importance, and farmers managed them with as much care and thought as the remainder of the farm.

13 Visual screening

12 Shelter and shade for livestock in winter and summer

11 Windbreaks protecting crops and stock

10 Help to control soil erosion from wind or leaching due to rain

7 Habitat for wildlife

8 Boundaries between soil types

9 Living fences to contain stock

11

WHAT IS A HEDGE TREE?

To explain what a hedge tree is, first a hedge must be defined. In Old English there was a variety of words for hedge: 'hegge' or 'hege' in Anglo Saxon and the Saxon word 'hecg' which is similar to 'haga' – an enclosure.

The simple question 'What is a hedge?' therefore elicits different answers in different parts of the country depending on the local history of land enclosure. In Cornwall a hedge can be an earth bank with stone sides; in Devon a hedge can be a high turf bank topped with a line of shrubs; in the Midlands a hedge can be a carefully managed low hawthorn structure; in Staffordshire a hedge can be made from holly, whilst in parts of Suffolk and Norfolk a hedge can be a line of gnarled pine trees. In Nottinghamshire fruit hedges can be dominated by damson and other Prunus species. Occasionally hedges can consist of exotic introduced plants – for example hedges near Ipswich which are composed of the Duke of Argyll's Tea Tree.

The Concise Oxford English Dictionary (1982) defined a hedge as:

"…a closely planted row of bushes or low trees especially forming (the) boundary of fields, gardens or roads; similar boundary of turf, stone etc"

This definition presumes that all hedges have been deliberately planted. Certainly during the Enclosure Period in the 17th and 18th centuries (see page 42), thousands of miles of hedges were planted, and although even today new ones are still being planted, hedges can also arise by other means (see page 14).

In recent hedgerow legislation, another Oxford English Dictionary definition (2nd edition, 1989) has been used to define a hedge:

"…a row of bushes forming a hedge, with the trees etc. growing in. For the purposes of the Regulations, the hedgerow does not have to contain trees, but any trees growing in it form part of the hedgerow. Where a former hedgerow has not been actively managed and has grown into a line of trees, it is not covered by the Regulations. However, trees in hedges may be protected by separate felling controls or by Tree Preservation Orders. The essential feature of a hedgerow is a row of bushes" (Hedgerow Regulations 1997) [1]

The government led Hedgerow Biodiversity Action Steering Group, defined a hedge as:

"...*any boundary line of trees or shrubs over 20m long and less than 5m wide, provided that at one time the trees or shrubs were more or less continuous. As stipulated in the Habitat Action Plan, where such lines of trees or shrubs are associated with features such as banks, walls, ditches, trees or verges, these features are considered to form part of the hedgerow.*" [2]

West Sussex County Council defines hedges in its Habitat Action Plan as:

"...*linear, landscape artefacts, consisting of woody shrub or tree species planted or managed mainly to confine domestic stock and to protect crops from grazing and browsing animals. They may also provide shelter and act as a barrier to soil erosion. The ecological attributes of our hedgerows have much in common with woodland edge habitat. In Sussex, hedgerows are frequently associated with ditches and banks and may include standard trees, historically grown as a source of timber and to provide shelter for domestic animals.*" [3]

The UK Biodiversity Steering Group for ancient and/or species-rich hedgerows produced a definition of a hedge tree as:

"...*any isolated tree, of whatever species, age or origin that has been deliberately or incidentally allowed to grow. Such trees should be integral to the hedge line and no more than 1 metre from the edge of the hedgerow.*" [4]

For the purposes of this book we have combined and condensed all the above definitions and consider a hedge to be:

"...*a linear landscape feature consisting of managed woody shrub and tree species, forming the boundary of fields, gardens or roads.*"

The following are therefore considered as hedge trees:

- an individual tree growing above a hedge

- a tree in a line of trees forming a hedge or boundary

- a tree, in a field, which is a relict of a previous hedge line. (This is a special category of hedge trees that are not fully covered in this book, but are nonetheless important trees in the landscape.)

HOW HEDGES HAVE ARISEN

Hedges have arisen in the British countryside in one of three ways. The oldest group – **ancient hedges** – are the result of clearance to create fields from wooded land. As the land was cleared, strips of woodland were left between the fields. These were then either left as woodland, as can still be seen in the 'shaws' of East Sussex and the Weald, or were managed into the more conventional image of a hedge. These types of hedge have the potential to be the most ecologically important, since the constituent ground flora and species composition could represent that of the original woodland from which they were carved.

The second group – **secondary hedges** – are those that have developed on land that has been cleared at one time, but then through neglect or change of use, has ceased to be managed. Here, through seeds born by birds or the wind, trees and shrubs have re-colonised the area, creating a new 'hedge'. The most obvious examples of this type are alongside abandoned railway lines, old fences and 'dead hedges' (fences made from woven hedge material) where the trees have re-colonised the area. Left alone they will become linear woodlands, or managed they could become a new hedge.

The final group – **planted hedges** – are the result of deliberate planting at some point in history. This group was increased considerably during the 'Enclosure period' (see page 42) which was when the first mass tree and shrub plantings took place. These Enclosure hedges led to the creation of a major nursery industry, designed to supply the massive quantities of shrubs needed to plant all the new hedges. They were largely created to mark ownership of the land, unlike the multi-purpose hedges of earlier times, and consequently few farmers regarded them as a source of fuel or food. Therefore they were largely planted as a monoculture of hawthorn or blackthorn and

A Devon hedgebank containing a great variety of ferns and wild flowers, including bluebells, making it possible that this hedge marks the edge of an ancient woodland.

occasionally with both. By 1770 "most major towns" [1] had nurseries capable of supplying the hawthorn needs of their area, and in consequence these 'mass produced' hedges lacked the local distinctiveness that would have resulted from the more localised seed gathering and sowing techniques of earlier generations.

Another period of hedge planting followed the spread of the railways across Britain as the track-bed had to be fenced or hedged to keep live-stock

off the lines. The late 19th century specification for the hedges around the Midland Railway was very detailed and involved the hawthorn being planted *"in parallel lines, the lines being 4 inches apart and the plants 8 inches from one to the other in rows. The planting is done so that one row is staggered with the other. …. The quicks are cut back at planting, left untrimmed till they attain a height of 6-8 feet, when they are layered, being subsequently trimmed in late autumn – early winter"* [2].

The Midland Railway and others also planted black poplar in these boundaries.

From the Enclosure period until the present, hedges have been planted by farmers across Britain, although on a more ad hoc basis. These hedges have often been of the 'largely hawthorn' type, although recent changes in planting ideas have focused on creating new hedges as conservation assets, often by planting a wider range of species.

DATING A HEDGE

In the 1960s Max Hooper, an ecologist working
for the Institute of Terrestrial Ecology,
published work suggesting a strong correlation
between the age of a hedge and the number of
woody species found in it. Taking the definitions
on page 14 – ancient, secondary and planted
hedges – one would therefore expect that the
ancient hedge would have more woody species
than the modern hedge, and generally speaking
this is the case.

Hooper's ideas were consolidated into "Hooper's
Rule or Hypothesis" [1] which stated that in 30
yards (27.4 metres) of hedge, every species
represents one century of age. Therefore a
hedge with four species in 30 yards would be
400 years old, eight species 800 years old.
Unfortunately this hypothesis was not confirmed
by subsequent empirical tests.

Although there is little doubt that ancient
hedges have the capacity to acquire a wide range
of species, the same effect can be achieved in
more recent hedges by planting a wide range of
trees and shrubs. Thus a 20 year-old hedge
planted with five or six species could mistakenly
be aged at 500 or more years old. Since hedges
are mostly the product of human intervention,
they owe their composition as much to the
economics of the farm as to their natural origins
and it is therefore probably wise to suppose that
trees were planted into the hedge structure.
As Miller said in 1741 [2], plant "with fruit trees",
the effect of which would be to add a notional
100 years to the age of the hedge for each new
fruit tree species.

Although Hooper's Rule is no longer promoted
as a method for dating hedges, the principle of
species richness as a guide to age is worth
considering further. Williamson (2002) [3] outlined
six types of hedges in Norfolk, as defined by their
species composition.

The wild service tree, on the left, is a woodland tree in a hedge situation; making it possible that this is a remnant edge of a medieval ancient woodland.

1. Hedges created around the large commons in approximately 1800. These are largely hawthorn, with some elder, sloe, rose and ash. There is also occasional elm. (Four to five woody species per 30 metres)

2. Hedges of the same general date and composition as 1, but which also include field maple. (Five to six woody species per 30 metres)

3. Hedges where the originally planted species – hawthorn or blackthorn – are still the dominant species, but where hazel, maple, holly and elm are well represented. (Evidence suggests that these hedges were created between 1300 and 1700 and contain five to eight species per 30 metres)

4. Hedges of early medieval origin along parish boundaries, some roads and in parishes which remained largely enclosed from an early date, where hawthorn and blackthorn are less dominant and maple, hazel and dogwood have become common. The dominance of these last three species has in fact decreased the overall species richness in some hedges, resulting in very low species counts in some places

5. Hedges similar to 4 but also containing small-leaved lime and wild service. These were probably created where areas of woodland were grubbed out in medieval or post medieval times

6. Modern hedges planted for nature conservation purposes with a wide range of species, which could be difficult to distinguish from medieval hedges in a hundred years' time

Williamson's results again show higher numbers of woody species in some older hedges, but not in others, and the group [4] hedges demonstrate the caution that is necessary with this method, for although these hedges are of considerable age, they may have only a limited range of species in a 30 metre stretch.

In assessing the age of a hedge, consideration must therefore be given to other factors including:

- mapped records of the area
- documentary evidence of the area
- archaeological evidence
- form of the boundary - straight hedge boundaries are often 18th century or later, wavy/curving hedges may be 17th century or earlier
- ancient trees in the hedge itself.

The last of these – the ancient trees – may yield useful evidence in dating the hedge, but again it will not be conclusive. For example, if there is a range of old pollards in a hedge, then it is likely that the hedge pre-dates the Enclosure period (after which pollarding was uncommon, see page 45).

Also, if the age of the trees in the hedge can be established, then the hedge is almost certain to pre-date the tree (working on the assumption that the tree grew in the hedge, not that the hedge grew to the tree).

However, this method can only establish the date before which the hedge was created. Thus if the tree is 300 years old, the hedge will be older, but it cannot be established from the tree whether the hedge is 301 years old or 1001 years old.

Too great a concentration on the specific age of the hedge is unhelpful, for although it is certainly desirable to know whether the hedge is ancient, secondary or planted, it is also important to know:

- if the hedge is species rich or species poor
- the role the hedge plays in the landscape or ecology of the area.

It is actually the combination of all these factors that makes one hedge of greater 'value' than another.

The Monnow Valley in the Welsh Borders, in winter, reveals various aspects of field boundaries and land management over the last 1,000 years. The sinuous hedges running down the hillside are of a much earlier vintage than the straight hawthorn hedges traversing the hill, which are probably post-18th century. Several old pollard trees are also discernible, which will have been used for many generations to supply fuel wood. In the foreground the light dusting of snow highlights the presence of medieval ridge and furrow (see page 41).

BRITAIN'S HEDGES AND HEDGE TREES

Hedgerow Structure

a Herbaceous
b Recently planted
c 1-2m
d 2-3m
e 3-4m
f 4-7m
g 7m+

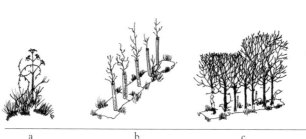

| a | b | c | d |

The hedge and hedge tree network throughout Britain has developed primarily as a product of land management – a tool to aid both farmers and landowners. However, in the process of creating hedges, farmers have also produced a rich network of habitats that can benefit the local plants and animals. For example, the Devon Hedge Group estimates that hedge habitat is possibly *"…the commonest and most widely distributed wildlife habitat in Devon, forming a dense and continuous web, across all but the highest ground in the county."* [1]

The biological value of the hedge and hedge trees to Britain's wildlife is immense. The UK Biodiversity Group have recorded over 600 plant species, 1500 insect species, 65 bird species and 20 mammal species living in hedges at some time [2]. There are even 13 species of plants and animals presently occurring in British hedges which are globally threatened or rapidly declining.

The reason that hedges and hedge trees are extremely important places for wildlife is that they provide a wide diversity of habitats in a relatively small area. Hedges can provide, shelter, breeding opportunities, nesting sites, song posts, hiding places, ecologically-friendly links between habitats and a range of other opportunities for wildlife.

The height of a hedge affects the species range and abundance of wildlife, and a recent paper produced by English Nature [3] shows some of the diversity of species related to the height of the vegetation (see above). This work suggests that for plants growing close to the hedge, the shorter the hedge the better, as this provides the maximum amount of light. Conversely the taller hedge is better for a wide range of birds and mammals. Therefore the hedge management regime can have a significant impact on the ecological value of the area as well as affecting the function of a hedge for agricultural purposes.

HEDGES ACROSS EUROPE

Particularly in England and Wales, hedges are such a familiar sight in the landscape that it is possible to think that the hedge is a part of the countryside everywhere. Elsewhere in Europe, however, hedges are by no means universal and hedged landscapes are found only in parts of France, northern Italy, the Austrian Alps, Greece, the Republic of Ireland, northern Spain and Romania. [4]

Article 10 of the European Communities Habitats Directive requires member states to *"to encourage the management of features of the landscape which are of major importance for wild fauna and flora. Such features are those which, by virtue of their linear and continuous structure (such as the traditional systems for marking field boundaries) or their function as stepping stones (such as ponds or small woods), are essential for the migration, dispersal and genetic exchange of wild species."* [5]

e   f   g

The EU therefore places particular importance on hedges in the European context as they can act as corridors for the protection and preservation of species. Britain, with its large network of hedges and hedge trees, thus has a major role to play in the conservation of this type of European, temperate climate, habitat.

a, b, c   The short hedge allows lots of light and is favoured by corn buntings, yellowhammers and grey partridge and plants such as purple ramping-fumitory (see page 27) may also be present.

d, e   As the hedge gets taller, species such as dormouse, turtle dove, red squirrel and Plymouth pear (see page 26) may be found.

f, g   The tallest hedges and lines of trees provide habitat for many bat species, owls, woodpeckers and tree sparrows.

The bocage of Europe, the landscape in which farmland is criss-crossed by hedges and trees, shown in green.

The way in which a hedge has been created affects its constituent tree species. The ancient hedges and 'shaws' potentially have the widest range of naturally occurring species, whilst the Enclosure or planted hedges have to rely on trees being planted or arriving by random agents such as wind blown seeds or imports by birds and mammals.

In ancient hedges, trees were selected and grown with a specific aim in mind. Oak, ash and elm were grown for timber and other purposes and appear to have been the commonest hedge trees, although the abundance of each changes from farm to farm and from district to district. Willows and poplars (both black and white) were also frequent hedge trees and all these species were often pollarded (see page 92). Some minor tree species including field maple, aspen, holly and hornbeam also appear to have been deliberately grown in hedges. In some places beech became a widespread hedge

tree: for example, Exmoor's landscape is famous for its 19th century beech hedges.

Along with the timber species, many fruit trees were also grown such as crab apple, wild cherry, hazel, elder and wild pear – the current distribution of the latter being now almost entirely confined to hedges [1]. These fruit trees provided food in the autumn when other food supplies were beginning

A multi-purpose damson hedge planted to provide food, drink and a dye from the fruits, shelter and an early source of nectar for local bees.

to run short and early writers extolled the virtues of "rosehip, crab apple and hazel" in hedges (Tussler 1573 [2] and Fitzherbert 1598 [3]) and Miller (1741) [4] suggested planting fruit trees. However there were other early writers who expressly suggested that species such as hazel should be avoided to thwart trespassers in search of nuts. [5]

Many of the flowers and fruits of the hedges were used for creating or flavouring alcohol. Blackberry wine, elderberry wine, sloe gin and vodka, cider, perry and verjuice (a kind of cider made from crab apples) were all made from hedge products. Many hedge plants also produced a range of dies and medicines which were invaluable to the farmer.

Despite the historical importance of hedge trees, their current status is difficult to define as figures are few and not necessarily comparable. One set of data, the Countryside Survey 2000 (CS 2000)[6], shows that in 1998 there were an estimated 1.8 million individual (isolated) hedge trees in Great Britain, 98% of which were found in England and Wales. This figure is around 3% lower than in the last survey in 1990, but is within the margins of sampling error, and therefore may not be significant. However, in the eastern lowlands of England an 8% decline is significant and appears to be at the expense of elm trees (*Ulmus* spp.)[7].

The commonest woody species in the CS 2000 samples was hawthorn which appeared in 90% of hedges, with blackthorn and elder occurring in 47% and 35% of hedges respectively. Overall, ash (*Fraxinus excelsior*) at 26% was the commonest tree with oak (*Quercus* spp) and field maple

(*Acer campestre*) next at 15% each. In Scotland, where the commonest species were ash and beech, hazel was almost absent. However hazel occurred in more than a quarter of hedges in England and nearly three quarters of those in Wales. Rowan was commonest in Welsh hedges, with the remaining relatively abundant tree being holly [7].

The survey also noted a wide range of other woody species including field-rose, grey willow, dogwood, goat willow, crab apple, wild cherry, alder, midland hawthorn, buckthorn, spindle, bird cherry, hornbeam, wayfaring-tree, guelder rose, yew, aspen, eared willow, wild service-tree, large-leaved lime, alder buckthorn, whitebeam, Sorbus intermedia agg and small-leaved lime [7].

In the CS2000 Survey, the majority of the trees recorded were over 20 years old, most falling into the '20 to 100 year' age category. The number of trees in the one to four year-old category had also declined significantly by around 40% since 1990 [7].

In contrast to the 1.8 million trees covered by the CS2000 Survey, the Forestry Commission Survey of 2001 showed that in England alone, there were 66 million live trees outside woodlands, which were either individual trees or in narrow linear features including hedges. The discrepancy between these two figures is a result of different definitions of hedge trees. However, despite the differences in actual numbers of trees, the Forestry Commission surveys since 1951 also show that there has been a decrease in the number of hedge and non-woodland trees during the period.

All the available data therefore suggest that our hedge tree stock is in decline. This can be attributed to specific causes such as Dutch elm disease and to changes in management techniques and agricultural need. This is a situation that can be remedied, but it will need concerted effort by a wide range of participants, coupled with an increased understanding of the role and value that hedge trees play.

The undulating countryside, typical of Herefordshire, reveals the range of hedge tree species and the abundance of mature trees.

WILDLIFE ASSOCIATED WITH HEDGES AND HEDGE TREES

The biological value of hedges and hedge trees to Britain's wildlife is enormous. They are important for moths (eg small eggar *Eriogaster lanestris*) and butterflies (eg hedge brown *Pyronia titonus*) and nearly half of the 46 species of butterfly found in lowland Britain breed in hedges, as do many birds, bats and dormice. Certain uncommon plants are also found in hedges, eg the Plymouth pear (*Pyrus cordata*) which grows only in a few hedges in south Devon and Cornwall, the endemic whitebeam (*Sorbus devoniensis*), and rare woodland-edge species such as crested cow-wheat (*Melampyrum cristatum*) which can be found in hedges in eastern England. Ancient hedges derived from woodland also contain a high diversity of plants including species such as wood sorrel (*Oxalis acetosella*), wood anemone (*Anemone nemorosa*) and bluebell (*Endymion non-scriptus*).

Over large stretches of intensively farmed Britain, hedges and their trees are an essential refuge for many plants and animals and can also act as corridors, allowing wildlife to move between habitats. The early leafing and flowering of many hedge trees and shrubs provides a valuable food source for insects in the spring, whilst trees such as oak, elm and ash can support large numbers of other species. For example throughout their range oaks support 500 insect species, elms 124 insect species and ash 68 species of invertebrate and over 200 species of lichen. The hedges' combination of shrub and tree species therefore provides opportunities for the huge range of life that hedges can support.

Rotting wood in living and standing dead trees in hedges is especially important for providing habitats for a wide range of dead-wood beetles such as lesser stag-beetle (*Dorcus parallelipipedus*) and others, some of which are particularly rare. Holes in hedge trees also provide nesting and sheltering opportunities for birds, including some rare and declining bird species. The tree sparrow (*Passer montanus*), song thrush (*Turdus philomelos*) and cirl bunting (*Emberiza cirlus*) are all species which have strong associations with hedge trees, but unfortunately populations of the first two have declined dramatically over the last few decades.

The rare white-spotted pinion moth (*Cosmia diffinis*) has declined due to Dutch elm disease and is now only reported frequently in Huntingdonshire. The larvae feed on the foliage of English elm (*Ulmus procera*) and wych elm (*U. glabra*) often in hedges.

The endemic Purple ramping-fumitory (*Fumaria purpurea*), is a species found in hedge-banks that have been recently disturbed by animals or machinery. It is concentrated in Cornwall and west Lancashire.

Of the 28 species of mammals, including badger (*Meles meles*), bank vole (*Clethrionomys glareolus*) and hedgehog (*Erinaceus europaeus*) which are found on lowland farms, most make some use of hedges for cover or as a corridor. Certain bat species use holes in trees and two rare bats, the barbastelle (*Barbastella barbastellus*) and Bechstein's (*Myotis bechsteinii*), are associated with ancient hedge trees. Bats including greater horseshoe (*Rhinolophus ferrumequinum*) natterer's (*Myotis nattereri*), whiskered (*Myotis mystacinus*) and Brandts' (*Myotis brandtii*) frequently fly along a regular 'beat' beside a tall hedge or woodland edge to catch their food, and the presence of trees in a hedge increases the range of insect species that the bats can catch. Many bat species use lines of trees and hedges to find their way and a gap of as little as 10 metres (33 feet) in a hedge may be enough to deter them from flying along it as they travel between roosts and feeding areas.

Plymouth pear (*Pyrus cordata*), one of Britain's rarest trees, found in hedges around Plymouth and Truro (opposite page).

Many rare bat species depend upon hedges and hedge trees.

Britain's hedges contain an important collection of mature, over mature and ancient trees. In fact 30% of the hedge tree population is over 100 years old (CS 2000). Part of the reason for this large percentage of old trees is the historical management that many received.

One of the main management techniques for hedge trees throughout history has been 'pollarding' – cutting the crown off a young tree at a height of 1.8 to 4.5 metres (6 to 15 feet) from the ground, leaving a permanent trunk called a 'bolling'. This trunk then sprouts a range of shoots at a height that keeps them away from grazing animals. In pollards, the constant cutting of the tree results in a characteristic shape, like a clenched fist, from which many young branches sprout. The new growth is then left to develop into 'poles' of a size suitable for use, which takes seven to 15 years depending on the use and the species.

The effect of pollarding on a tree is curious, as it often allows the tree to reach a much greater age than if it were left to grow into its normal mature shape. Pollarding retains the tree in a state of greater vitality by interrupting the normal aging process and, since the crown is smaller, also reduces the likelihood of storm damage. Pollarding trees has therefore allowed many to grow for several hundred years and some for much longer.

The abundance of ancient hedge pollards is by no means universal. While they exist in their thousands in East Anglia, there are fewer in other parts of the country, although their true distribution is still not fully known.

HISTORY

During the second half of the 18th century, these ancient hedge trees were used by the great landscape designers of the time. To allow grand new landscapes to be created, which carried with them a feeling of age and continuity, the designers

– Humphry Repton, Lancelot 'Capability' Brown and others – used these old trees to their advantage. To create an 'instant park', which had the feeling of antiquity, these designers carefully removed the hedges from around the ancient trees, leaving them free-standing in the landscape:

"the inclosure hedges should be removed: …to take the best advantage of those trees or bushes which grow in the hedge, and at the same time to obliterate every remembrance of the hedge." (Humphry Repton's Landscape Plans for Hanslope Park 1792).

The medieval deer park at Moccas in Herefordshire with ancient oaks employed in 'Capability' Brown's landscape scheme.

Repton's views of the management of many of these hedge trees was however fairly scathing, so he would have only used those that suited his purpose:

"A tree to the Landlord at a distance is valuable for its Timber, to the man of Taste and the Gentleman it is an object of beauty, but to the farmer it is only considered for those branches to which he claims a right as faggot wood for his oven. …In such hands it is rather a matter of wonder that the trees have not been more disfigured, than that any should have been cut pruned and mutilated as we here see them in the hedge rows." (Humphry Repton's Landscape Plans for Hanslope Park 1792).

Over the last two hundred years, the general absence of management of many hedges has led, in some extreme cases, to the hedge being removed or so neglected that only odd trees remain scattered amongst the fields. These field trees are important both ecologically and for landscape reasons. However, like many of the trees still standing in hedges, they have suffered from neglect and the lack of a strategy for their succession.

'BRITAIN'S MOST IMPORTANT ECOLOGICAL ASSETS'

Field trees, ancient hedge trees left in parklands and those still growing in hedges have become the source of much conservation interest over the last few years. They are now acknowledged as providing unique habitats for a wide range of rare and unusual species, and have been referred to by some contemporary writers as among Britain's most important ecological assets [1].

The value of old trees is that they retain large quantities of decaying wood within the structure of the hedge which provides valuable habitats for rare and endangered fungi, lichens and invertebrates plus roost and nest sites for bats, birds and other small mammals. Even a single ancient hedge tree can host rare and endangered species, providing a huge range of micro-habitats, as can be seen from the illustration.

There are more than 1800 different invertebrate species in Britain which are dependent on decaying wood, about 6% of the entire British invertebrate fauna [2].

For these creatures a large standing living tree with columns of decay in the heartwood is a crucial resource. In the early stages of decomposition, rotting heartwood provides food for the larvae of species such as the lesser stag beetle and rhinoceros beetle (*Sinodendron cylindricum*), whilst colourful insects like the red net-winged beetle (*Platycis minutes*) can feed on the rotting heartwood of beech and ash.

As the tree further decomposes a different fauna develops, including the hairy fungus beetle (*Mycetophagus piceus*), and the larvae of the rare noble chafer (*Gnorimus nobilis*) which can occasionally be found developing in hollowing fruit trees, oaks and willows [3].

In rotting trees the end product accumulates in the bottom of the hollow trunk. Some of Britain's rarest insects develop in this environment of relatively constant temperature and humidity, protected from the outside world by the surrounding living trunk tissues. The darkling beetle (*Prionychus ater*) is one of the most widespread specialists while the rare violet click beetle (*Limoniscus violaceus*) is one of Britain's very few legally protected beetles [3].

The adults of many insects that develop in decaying wood need nearby blossom on which to feed before they can start to reproduce. Blossom provides nectar – an energy-rich food – and pollen which provides the energy needed for egg production. Blossom can be important throughout the spring, and species such as sallow, holly, privet, rowan, crab apple, wild pear, guelder rose, bramble are all beneficial.

Flowering trees and shrubs are by far the most important sources of nectar and pollen to these creatures. Insects in ancient hedge trees have easy access to a whole range of species, especially hawthorn which provides the ideal insect blossom, partly due to its flowering in late spring when so many wood-decay insects are in the adult stage.

Unfortunately as an old tree becomes senile, it declines and decays. Many ancient trees grow along roadsides and highways, where falling deadwood or limbs may be a hazard to passing traffic or pedestrians. These trees need careful management to ensure safety whilst retaining them and their unique ecological values. The Tree Council has a range of member organisations which can provide specialist advice. These include the Ancient Tree Forum, the Arboricultural Association and the Tree Advice Trust. Details of these organisations can be obtained from the Tree Council or from its website **www.treecouncil.org.uk**

Longhorn beetle (*Stenocorus meridianus*) and lasius ants (*Lasius fuliginosus*): two of Britain's rare insect species, which are associated with hedge tree deadwood.

VARIOUS HABITATS IN A VETERAN TREE

1   Snag/stub.

2   Crown limb
    – small cavities.

3   Crown limb
    – large cavity.

4   Lightning strike.

5   Woodpecker hole.

6   Established sap run.

7   Old wound with scar tissue
    and loose bark.

8   Bracket fungi.

9   Fungal colonisation of roots.

10 Fallen limb.

11 Rot hole in trunk.

12 Basal cavity.

13 Branch reaching ground.

14 Bark with fungal infection.

15 Suspended broken limb.

16 Subsiding major limb.

17 Delamination of wood.

18 Major deadwood.

HEDGE TREES AND THE LANDSCAPE

From the mountains of Scotland to the marshes of the English south coast, the landscape of Britain is rich and diverse – a mixture of landform, local biodiversity, land use and human history. Even within small areas, huge changes can be seen. In Hampshire, for example, a 40-mile drive north travels from salty coastal marshes, through chalk downland, clay vales, back on to the chalk and then to heathland.

In the latter half of the 1990s, English Nature and the Countryside Agency set about defining England's different landscape characteristics, an initiative which led to the mapping of England into 159 separate, distinctive Landscape Character Areas [1]. They defined the specific landscape features of each area and produced historical evidence of the factors that led to the current appearance of the countryside.

In 38 areas (about a quarter of the countryside), hedge trees, shelterbelts and 'shaws' on the boundaries of fields were considered to be essential features of the landscape. Here are some examples.

- In the Blackmoor Vale and the Vale of Wardour, Somerset, where small, rectilinear pasture fields have hedge oak trees

- On Exmoor where extensive 19th century moorland-edge enclosures and farms have beech-topped hedgebanks and beech windbreaks

- In the Marshwood and Powerstock Vales, Dorset, where the pasture vale landscape has ribbons of woodland, regular field patterns and abundant hedge oaks

- The Vale of Taunton which has variable hedge tree cover, but with some areas of abundant hedge oaks

- In Buckinghamshire, where the Vale is a predominantly pastoral landscape including regular fields within a well-defined network of trimmed hedges often with oak/ash hedge trees and some small blocks of woodland

- In the South Hampshire Lowlands where oaks are prevalent within hedges and woodlands and help to create an impression of a well-wooded landscape

- South Norfolk is an area of relatively small, individual landholdings, with scattered small parkland estates – a mixture of remnant medieval Ancient Countryside (irregular small fields with pollard hedge oaks), early co-axial field patterns east of Scole (with two parallel sides and the other sides varying in angle) and large modern fields devoid of hedges and trees

- In South Suffolk where the principal hedge tree is elm (with some hornbeam). Elsewhere in Suffolk ash predominates, while in Essex oak is common. Ancient coppice woods and typical patterns of

copses are connected by hedges. Trees and woods appear to join together to give a wooded skyline

- In the Bowland Fringle, Lancashire, where the intensively managed landscape, with lush hay meadows in small- to medium-scale fields, is defined by well maintained hedges with mature hedge trees

- In the Eden Valley where mature hedges, hedge trees, small copses and shelterbelts contribute to the well-wooded character of the area

- In Shropshire, Cheshire and Staffordshire where the sandstone ridges have field boundaries which are predominantly hedges, generally well managed, with abundant hedge trees, mostly oak

- South Herefordshire which has a population of ageing hedge trees

Not surprisingly the majority of these Landscape Character Areas are in the 'Ancient Countryside' (see page 40). However it is significant that so much of the modern character of the countryside is in part defined by our hedge trees. Lack of management and failure to replace the hedge tree population (see page 22) could therefore result not only in the loss of the trees themselves, but could irrevocably change the character of a large percentage of the British countryside.

Old beech hedge on Shoulsbury Common, on the edge of Exmoor.

As well as being important in defining the landscape of Britain, there are also throughout Britain, a series of local variations in hedge types. This has led to a significant number of regionally distinctive hedge types. A recent review undertaken by the Countryside Agency [1] outlined the following locally specific hedge types.

Elm hedges. Usually single species or dominated by suckering shoots of Ulmus species, particularly English elm (Ulmus procera). Examples can be found in coastal Suffolk; central Worcestershire and on the Isle of Sheppey, northern Kent.

Holly hedges. Commonly 5 to 10 metre (16 to 32 feet) sections of holly, and whole field boundaries or medieval deer park boundaries as sole dominant species. Examples can be found in the Dedham Vale, Suffolk; around Ampthill and Woburn, Bedfordshire and in the Peak District.

Single species beech hedges. Often on banks, either close clipped or now grown into a line of mature trees. Pioneered as a hedge shrub during the late Enclosure period. Examples can be found on Exmoor, Somerset; near Bodmin, Cornwall; and scattered throughout the south west.

Hazel-dominated hedges which form small field patterns on the forest margins. Forest of Dean, Gloucestershire.

Willow hedges and scrub banks. Thought to result from the local basket making industry. These can be found in the Trent Valley, Staffordshire and Nottinghamshire.

Mixed hedges with willow and alder in valley bottoms. These can be found in Dentdale and Deepdale, Yorkshire and around the Humber.

Fruit hedges. Dominated by damson, cherry plum and sloe, wild plum, crab apple and other Prunus species. Examples can be found in central Nottinghamshire; around the Malvern Hills, and Bromyard Downs, Worcestershire and Herefordshire, and in the Hertfordshire parish of Clothall Bygrave.

Elm hedge in East Anglia and a damson hedge in Herefordshire.

Cornish hedgebank with tamarisk (opposite page).

Windswept hedges composed of various species – usually gorse, hawthorn, blackthorn or elm. Examples can be found on coasts and exposed plateaux of Cornwall and the north east, e.g. Flamborough Head, plus European gorse hedges which are either naturally occurring or remnants of scrub cover cleared from heath vegetation. Examples can be found scattered along the south coast including Poole.

EXOTIC HEDGES

Tamarisk hedges. A non-native shrub planted because of its salt-tolerance. Examples can be found in coastal areas of Hampshire, Dorset, Devon and Cornwall.

'Exotic' pittosporum, evergreen spindle and fuchsia hedges. Planted to shelter crops. Examples can be found in the Scilly Isles and Cornwall.

Lilac hedges. Local and scattered type, with lilac dominating a mixed hedge. Examples are found in coastal Suffolk and the Sheringham area of Norfolk.

Hedges with Duke of Argyll's Tea Tree. Very local hedge type – visually distinctive. Examples can be found in the Suffolk Sandlings and near Ipswich.

LINES OF TREES

Pine hedges. Planted and managed as hedges during the Enclosure period then left unmanaged, resulting in contorted shapes. Examples can be found in Breckland and central East Anglia.

Shaws. Wide, mixed linear remnant /relict woodlands. Examples can be found in the High and Low Weald, Sussex and Kent.

Monterey cypress windbreaks. Examples can be found on Hayling Island, Hampshire and in other south coastal areas of Britain.

Alder and poplar and willow windbreaks. Tall, closely planted shelterbelts. Examples can be found as boundaries to orchards and hop gardens in Kent and Surrey.

Distinctive earth banks with windswept oak trees. Examples can be found on the Norfolk coast.

Hedgebanks. Usually stone faced with an earth core. Sometimes topped by trees and shrubs, gorse and hawthorn. Examples can be found in south west England.

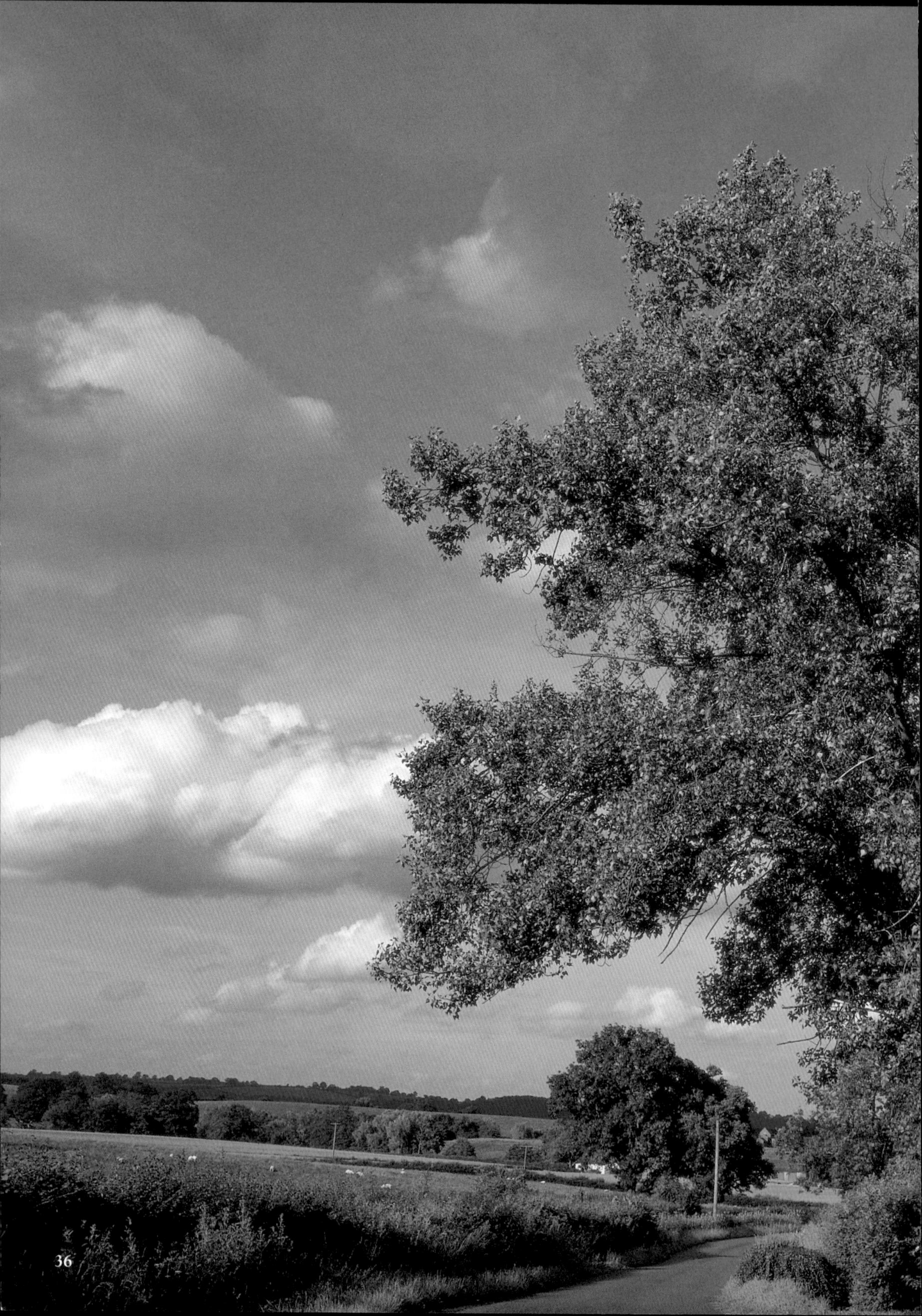

At the end of the last Ice Age, 15000 years ago, the British landscape was largely covered in snow and ice and only a few alpine plants lived in the cold summers. As the snow and ice retreated, Britain was colonised by plants creating a landscape similar to the arctic tundra of modern day Greenland. At that time (c. 9000 years ago), Britain was still connected to mainland Europe, allowing the free movement of plants, and animals, including humans over the whole continent.

As the climate warmed, the first tree and shrub species began to arrive. Pollen analysis shows that the early trees arriving back in Britain led eventually to the creation of a well wooded British landscape, often referred to as the 'Wildwood'. Recent research by Frans Vera in the Netherlands [1], has suggested that at this time Europe's large herbivores opened – or kept open – grassy patches in forests and it is now thought that the wild ox or auroch (*Bos primigenius*, the native ancestor of domestic cattle), along with elk (*Akes akes*), beaver (*Castor fiber*) and wild boar (*Sus scrofa*) influenced the structure and ecology of these original wild forests.

Between 8000 and 7500 years ago, the sea level rose sufficiently to sever the land bridge between Britain and mainland Europe. The countryside would have become largely wooded, with the clear areas being a result of poor soils, coastal location, animal clearings, bogs and open water. The early Mesolithic settlers of these islands were thought to be largely coastal dwellers and beachcombers, who maintained a 'wandering' lifestyle, making a living wherever they could find food.

However, recent evidence from Portland, in Dorset [2], of an 8000 year old midden (a rubbish dump consisting of limpets and other molluscs – all in a matrix of clayey loam mixed with charcoal), hearths and a cooking/storing pit raises the possibility that even these early people

led a settled lifestyle, possibly all the year round. A limited analysis of charcoal pieces from this midden has produced the remains of wild cherry, crab apple, pear and hazel nuts, showing that these early people had already begun to use Britain's tree products.

A Cornish 'hedge' at Zennor.

Wild Boar (*Sus scrofa*).

During the Neolithic period (6000 to 4000 years ago), arriving settlers brought with them crops and animals and began farming Britain. They converted large tracts of the countryside to farmland and established settled farmsteads.

At this time in Cornwall, the first Cornish 'hedges' enclosed land for cereal crops. Prehistoric farms were then about 5 to 10 hectares (12 to 25 acres), with fields typically of about 0.1 hectares (0.25 acre), suitable for hand cultivation. The typical Cornish hedge is a hybrid between a stone wall and an earth bank. It has an earth core, faced each side with local stone, usually tapered from the base to half-way up, the top being half the

width of the bottom. This is vital for the stability of the hedge structure. The stone hedge is similar in shape to drystone walls in other parts of Britain, except that its sides have an inward curve [3].

Between 4000 and 3000 years ago, Bronze Age systems of farming became well developed. The wildwood had been progressively felled and probably covered only about 50% of the country by this time. Complex field systems were created in some parts of the country, and the Land's End peninsula still provides a clear image of this early countryside. At Zennor for example, small irregular fields have retained their original prehistoric shape and boundaries, with Cornish 'hedges' comprised of massive granite block walls and earth banks, made from rocks cleared from the fields.

Elsewhere in Britain during the same period, areas of the countryside were laid out in co-axial fields (with two parallel sides and the other sides varying in angle), typified by the low stony banks or 'reaves' of Dartmoor.

Whilst the Zennor and Dartmoor early field systems have survived intact, the evidence that living hedges existed around early fields is obviously harder to obtain. Nevertheless in Suffolk, Norfolk, Essex, Kent and Hertfordshire, hedged co-axial, reave-like field systems, are still apparent and the boundaries of these fields may have remained largely unchanged for millennia [4].

Unfortunately much of this period of our landscape history inevitably remains vague as the small human population and absence of records leaves us with only tantalising glimpses into the past. However, it is amazing that in certain parts of Britain field systems and boundaries established over 6000 years ago still remain and influence the nature of the modern countryside.

ROMAN HEDGES
AND HEDGE TREES

Around 1900 years ago (100AD), the influence of the Romans was becoming widespread throughout Britain. The Romans had a long tradition of hedging, preferring a living hedge to a constructed fence, because of its greater permanence [1].

With their innovative ideas the Romans improved ploughs and scythes, thereby raising their productivity and so helping to feed the increasing population, some of whom began to move to the new towns. By this time the woodlands had been reduced to a national cover of approximately 11% (similar to today) with little remaining wildwood. The residual woodland was managed, especially through coppicing, with hedges and fences enclosing fields close to settlements and farmsteads.

By 400AD there was a significant urban population engaged in trades and crafts and no longer directly involved in agriculture. This period also saw the extensive development of Roman villas, properties owned by local magnates and often surrounded by thousands of acres of land. As a result of these changes there was a corresponding increase in new hedges and fences to enclose larger rectangular fields or to mark boundaries, some of which can still be seen in south east Essex [1].

ANGLO SAXON AND
MEDIEVAL HEDGES

During the Saxon period (6th to 11th centuries) many of the changes created by the Romans were reversed, with town dwellers moving back to the countryside and re-adopting subsistence farming methods. This coincided with a large scale depopulation of Britain as a result of war, disease and emigration. The effect of the population decline was that areas of the countryside reverted to woodland and scrub.

Throughout Europe, even in the 15th century, there was a complicated mixture of 'live' and 'dead' hedges interspersed with hedge trees.

It appears that hedges became increasingly common during this period, often being used to define fields and land holdings in an unstable political environment. Then, during the late Saxon period, a change occurred which had a dramatic effect on the agricultural landscape – the 'open field' system was adopted, although the reasons are not fully understood. Open field areas became known as 'Champion' districts, while the areas that retained their earlier hedged or walled field systems subsequently became known as the 'Ancient' countryside [1].

The Champion districts covered an area from Yorkshire through the Midlands and into parts of Somerset and Dorset. Farmsteads and scattered

period 'dead hedges' appear to have been an important part of agriculture for many centuries. By 1601 Barnaby Googe [2] referred to two types of hedging – *"the live hedge of thorn set on a bank above a ditch and laid periodically"*, and the other *"the common hedge of dead wood, well staked and thick plashed"*.

Interestingly the 15th century French picture shows a mixture of 'live' and 'dead hedging', and also includes more permanent trees in the 'dead hedge' line, suggesting that these apparently temporary markers may have been used on boundaries that were semi-permanent.

Between the furlongs and fields, along the boundaries of townships and surrounding the townships themselves, live hedges remained or were created, but their abundance was greatly reduced compared with the Ancient countryside areas.

Between 1315 and 1350 Britain was struck by famine and the plague which reduced the UK population by 50 %, resulting in abandonment of agriculture from many marginal farming lands. Within decades, scrub replaced previously cultivated and grazed land and new woodlands formed, many of which remain today as ancient semi-natural woodland.

By 1400 the majority of the population was still engaged in subsistence agriculture which occupied nearly all usable land. Through the 15th and 16th centuries rising demand for firewood and charcoal placed increasing pressure on woodlands, although their area remained broadly stable at around 10%. This period also saw the beginnings of the practice of enclosure (see page 42) that would continue through several centuries, creating tens of thousands of miles of new hedge. As the total length of hedge continued to grow, the number of hedge trees also began to increase as a source of wood fuel.

hamlets from earlier times were replaced with small nucleated villages, with hedges and small fields close to the townships. These 'close in' areas were surrounded by large swathes of unhedged open fields consisting of plots of land divided into complex holdings by the residents of each township.

The land was divided into strips of between a quarter and half an acre called 'sellions'. Groups of sellions created a 'furlong' and groups of furlongs made a 'field'. Within the fields, the nature of the intensive ploughing which produced what is now referred to as 'ridge and furrow' prevented hedges from developing.

However, 'dead hedging' with woven fences of hazel and willow allowed the demarcation of land holdings within the fields. During the Saxon

This 19th century plate shows one of the purposes of hedges, as jumps for the hunting fraternity. The riders appear to be jumping out of woodland, over a hedge. Note the presence of large hedge trees.

17TH, 18TH AND 19TH CENTURY HEDGES

Almost all the maps of the 17th century show parishes across England having some length of hedge. By the 18th century, reforms of agricultural practices paved the way for the Industrial Revolution and had two major effects: they increased the output of farms and reduced the number of people who needed to work on the land, resulting in a movement from the countryside to the towns where there was employment in the emerging industries.

To allow farmers to farm in the new ways they needed large, consolidated plots of land instead of the scattered 'strip' system that had previously been practised in the open field or Champion districts. As a result Parliament enacted a series of laws (mostly between 1760 and 1830) called the Enclosure Acts, to consolidate land holdings and to specify that the enclosed land was surrounded by hedges and ditches.

The 5,000 separate Enclosure Acts enclosed over seven million acres of open fields or common land. Rackham [1] estimates that over 200,000 miles of new hedge were planted between 1750 and 1850. The percentage of the open field land that was enclosed varied considerably across the country. This suited wealthy landowners with sporting interests. For example, in Northamptonshire 51% of the open fields were enclosed, while in Shropshire only 0.3% were enclosed [2].

The speed and scale of hedge establishment in this period led to the creation of large commercial nurseries specialising in the supply of hedging material, mostly hawthorn, to create the new network of hedges.

Writing in 1741 Philip Miller [3] said, *"where Land is properly enclosed and the hedge-rows planted with Timber-trees, it preserves the land warm, and defends and shelters it from the violent cold nipping winds, which in severe Winters frequently destroys much of the corn, pulses or whatever grows in the open fields… The hedges and trees also afford shelter for the cattle from the cold winds in the winter and also shade for them from the great heats of Summer."*

The spread of Enclosure, particularly in the open field systems of the Midlands, led to the creation

20TH CENTURY HEDGES

From 1870 until 1940, agriculture hit a period of recession, as America began to flood European markets with a glut of cheap grain. Farming neglected the poorer land and the countryside reverted to a wilder state than it had been for many centuries. Hedges were managed less frequently and there was a significant emergence of hedge trees as hedge management declined. However, from 1940 to the end of the 20th century agriculture fortunes changed again with a period of expansion, enhanced by entry into the EEC in 1973. Arable farming and its intensification led to the development of larger machinery, making much bigger fields an economic necessity. As a result, hedges suffered and estimates suggest that between 1946 and 1970 some 4,500 miles of hedge were removed every year.

After the Second World War the development of suburbs and new towns led to the expansion of urban hedges in parks and gardens. Today these hedges and their trees play an increasingly important part in bringing nature into towns.

In the 20 years following 1965, there was a resurgence of Dutch elm disease and, due to the importation of a more virulent strain of the disease, most of the countryside's most significant hedge elms were lost.

It is currently estimated that the UK's total length of hedges is about 280,000 miles, of which about 42% or 118,000 miles are ancient and/or species-rich (and hence probably pre-Enclosure). Such hedges are still concentrated in the Ancient countryside areas – in southern England, especially in the south west, and in southern Wales – but they are relatively scarce in Scotland.

of many new, often very straight, hawthorn hedges which divided up the countryside geometrically. These hedges were 'quickset', a word which indicates both the hedge itself and the act of planting it. They cut across the open field ridge and furrow system, and many of the fields that had previously been ploughed were converted to arable pasture. As the landscape changed, fox-hunting began to spread especially in the Midland areas of Rutland, Leicestershire, Northamptonshire and Buckinghamshire. This had a knock-on effect on hedge management as dense low growing 'walls' of vegetation were desirable as jumps for riders. These tidy, well managed hedge 'jumps' are still a feature of many hedges today.

WRITTEN HISTORY

Unfortunately the earliest history of hedge trees was not recorded and not until the Anglo-Saxon charters were there any specific references to hedge trees being used as boundary markers. Rackham (1986) [1] tells of 787 trees named in these charters, usually in hedges, and gives an example from Havant, Hampshire in 980 where the boundary ran *"through the middle of Hill-lea to the old ash; from the ash south over the road to the apple tree; from the apple tree to the white hazel."*

Navigating by using trees as waypoints appears to have been commonly practised throughout history and indeed in modern day Zambia, for example, it is still the main method in many areas of rough bush-land.

It is of course vital that trees used for navigation must be easily distinguishable throughout the year to avoid confusion. In the Anglo Saxon charters oak and ash were commonly mentioned, as were apple, willow and alder. There were also references [1] to distinctive trees such as 'hoar-trees' (probably trees with beard-like lichens), 'crooked trees', 'prostrate oaks', 'footy oaks' (large based) and 'ivied alder', as well as occasional references to sacred trees, such as the 'Epistle Oak' at Ringwood, Hampshire.

The first reference to an English hedge tree in literature appears to come from the beginning of the 13th century in a Middle English poem, written probably by Nicholas de Guildford of Dorsetshire, which describes a debate between the sober owl and the merry nightingale in a thick neglected hedge near Portesham in Dorset, the owl sitting in an ivy covered tree, the nightingale in a beech and another character, a wren, sitting in a lime (lynde) tree.

View of Henley-on-Thames by Jan Siberechts, circa 1690, showing an abundance of hedge trees.

THE MIDDLE AGES ONWARDS

During the Middle Ages, records of hedge trees increased, especially in disputes and court cases, but the most detailed records date from the 16th and 17th centuries.

From the 16th century onwards, estate maps and landscape paintings show that trees in hedges were abundant in some parts of the countryside. Estate records often show that there were large numbers of hedge trees and on some estates thousands of trees were recorded. In the 1740s one estate in Suffolk (Thorndon) had

exceptionally 6,058 pollarded hedge trees on 187 acres (75 hectares) – over 30 per acre (75 per hectare) [1]. Although such high density was probably rare, early painters of the English landscape depict views with large numbers of hedge trees and this painting of Henley-on-Thames, by Jan Siberechts circa 1690, shows clearly a pastoral landscape, where the hedges are full of well spaced trees.

From the middle of the 18th century until 1800, especially as a consequence of changes in ownership during the Enclosure period, there was a decline in the number of hedge trees in some areas of the country. Elsewhere, particularly in Scotland, hedge trees seem to have become relatively abundant, perhaps for the first time. This period saw a decline in the popularity of pollards and few new ones were created over the next two centuries. Many of the existing pollards were also neglected.

The decline in numbers of hedge trees seems to have continued until the latter half of the 19th century, as farming traditions changed, and by 1870 hedge tree numbers had hit a low point. Farm incomes then began to fall and over the next 80 years decreasing wealth on the farm resulted in an increase in hedge trees as fewer hedges were managed or destroyed.

THE PRESENT SITUATION

In 1951 the Forestry Commission conducted its most thorough census of hedge trees and estimated that there were 73 million hedge and park trees in England, Scotland and Wales. There were, however, some major differences in the abundance of saplings in hedges discovered around the country by this survey, which led to the creation of the Merthyr Committee in 1955. The committee expressed concern about the proportion of saplings [2] in relation to mature trees, suggesting that the tree population should comprise 6 saplings to 3 small trees, 2 medium sized and 1 large tree. In fact, the actual population was 2 saplings to 1 small tree, 1 medium sized and 1 large tree. By the time of the next census in 1965 the ratio had declined to 1:1:1:1, suggesting that only one sixth of the necessary saplings existed to create the next generation of hedge trees.

The increasing intensification of agriculture towards the latter half of the 20th century resulted in the loss of thousands of miles of hedges, along with millions of hedge trees. The Dutch elm disease outbreak of the late 1960s onwards removed some 20 million elms from our countryside, mostly from hedges. Add to this the increasing mechanisation of hedge cutting over the last 20 years, with hedges now often being cut annually and with no thought for the next generation of hedge trees, and the future of hedge trees may be looking bleaker than at any previous point in their history.

Badly flailed hedge (above).

Well trimmed hedge (right), with fine old oaks and a young holly in the foreground – a good example of mixed age hedge trees.

THE FUTURE FOR HEDGE TREES

The future for hedge trees depends on the present generation valuing such trees for their contribution to our environment, to the farm and to the continuing life of our countryside. It also requires an understanding of the practices used to create and manage a landscape with hedge trees in it, as well as re-valuing the role the trees play.

Without a shift in our understanding of the significant role of hedge trees in the countryside and an appreciation of their place in British life, survival of hedge trees through the 3rd millennium may not be achieved. However with care, appreciation and concerted effort we can continue to benefit from our tree heritage, whilst shaping a new landscape for the future.

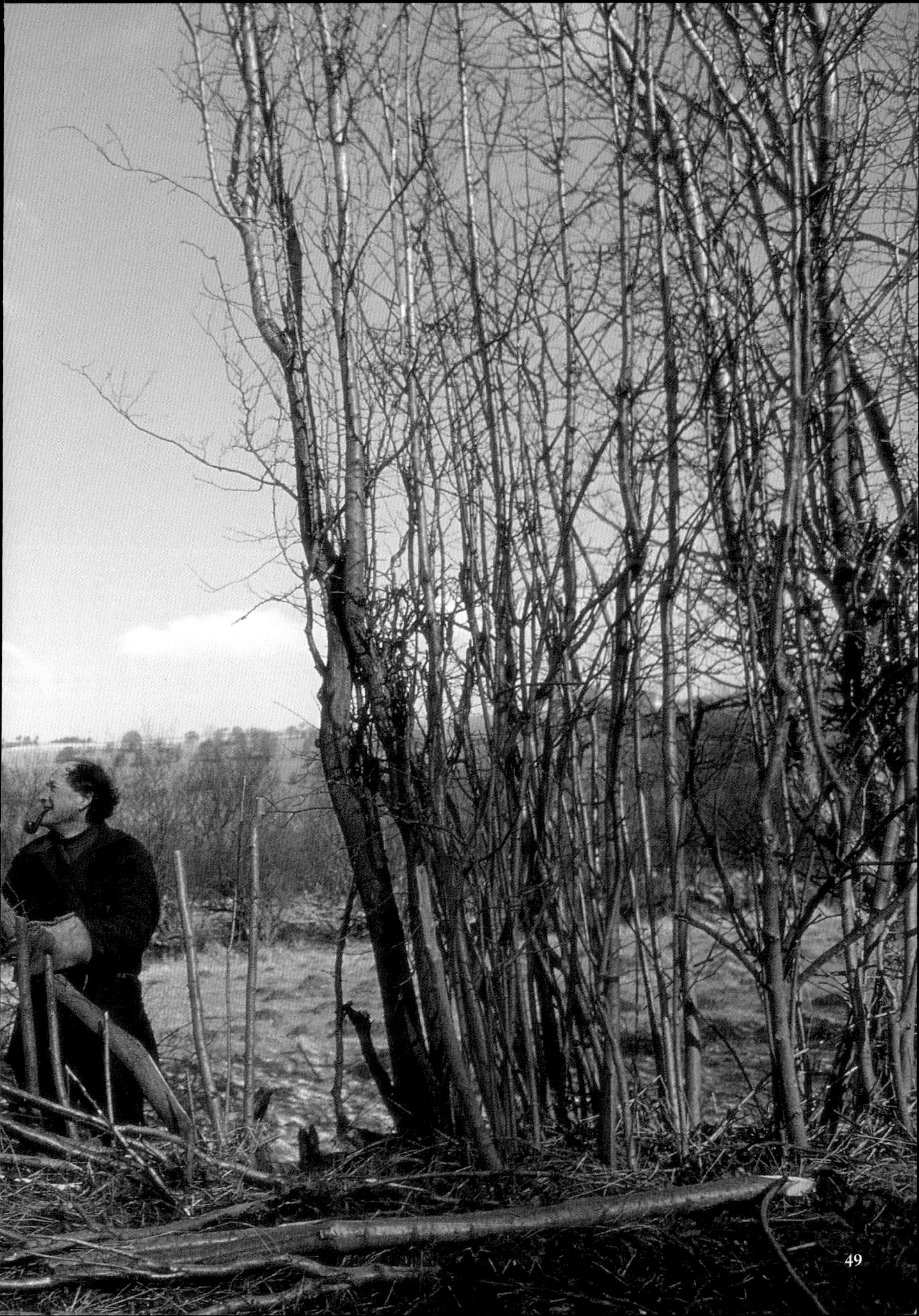

HEDGE TREE AND HEDGE MANAGEMENT

Once a hedge of any length has been created, its management depends on its uses. As shown on page 10 a hedge can provide one or many of these features:

- shelter and shade for livestock
- firewood and timber
- food and medicines
- a boundary marker
- living fences to contain stock
- jumps for horse riding
- a windbreak to protect crops and stock
- a link between other elements in the landscape such as woods, which can be valuable for wildlife
- habitat for wildlife
- visual screening
- cover for game species
- visual feature to enhance a roadside or house
- control of soil erosion from wind or leaching due to rain

Hedges, throughout history, have been managed to provide a range of several such uses although each of these can require a different management technique. For example, a tightly clipped low hawthorn hedge of the type suitable for horse riding jumps would not be a good source of firewood.

Farm managers have generally inherited hedges and managed them in a suitable way to meet their needs. The ancient multi-purpose hedges were often allowed to grow quite high before being cut for timber. Some were also wide, probably being linear thickets rather than 'tidy' hedges. Unfortunately our knowledge of the management of pre-Enclosure hedges is slim and lies in court cases and parish records.

Recently laid hedge (left), with new trees planted in front. The hedge layer has wisely protected the hedge from browsing livestock with a temporary wire fence. The large old ash pollard (below) has been regularly harvested for fuel wood.

These show that people *"stole thorns from their neighbours' hedges"* (1283 Court Roll) [1]; *"planted hedges"* (1330 estate accounts) [1]; and were put in the stocks for *"breaking any hedge or stealing wood"* (1567 Court Roll) [1]. Nevertheless the specific shapes, heights and techniques for managing these hedges remain shrouded in mystery.

Pollard (1974) [2] suggests that early mixed hedges – as typified by those still found in the south east and south west – were probably managed, as were the woods, by coppicing. Coppicing the hedge every 7 to 15 years, yielded the wood products and firewood that the farmers needed, whilst allowing timber trees and ancient pollards to continue to grow. During the first years after coppicing the fields were turned to arable crops, then as the hedges grew and became or were made stock-proof, the land was turned to grass and stock was kept in the field until the next coppicing.

According to Pollard [2], hedge laying was practised relatively little until the 18th and 19th centuries, although the craft may have its origins much earlier than this. Beddall (1950) [3] showed that during the 18th and 19th centuries farm leases included clauses dealing with the special care of hedges and gates. For example, on the Hawstead Estate, Suffolk, in 1732, the tenant was allowed *"bushes and stakes for hedge repair"*, while in a Warwickshire lease of 1786 the tenant was *"when required to cut and plash the hedges and make ditches 3 feet by 2 feet, or pay or cause to be paid to the landlord one shilling per rood for such as shall not be done after three months notice has been given in writing"* [3].

As the practise of hedge laying extended across Britain, this became a skilled and vital craft, and the hedge-layer became a valued member of the local economy.

HEDGE LAYING

Midland style of hedge laying

The effect of specialised hedge laying craftsmen being available to provide cost effective hedge management, meant that hedge laying as a technique spread across Britain. Then local circumstances and agricultural need, combined with individual hedgers skills and the tree species in the hedge, dictated the style of hedge laying that was adopted. The main styles of hedge laying that now exist are:

- **Midland style** – designed to keep heavy bullocks in their field. This style is found mainly in Leicestershire, Northamptonshire, Oxfordshire and Warwickshire. Here the hedge slopes towards the animals, stakes are driven in behind the line of the roots, and strong binding is used below the top of the hedge, so that bullocks cannot twist it off with their horns.

- **Welsh style and south western style** – developed mainly to control sheep, the hedges are frequently grown on a bank which helps to give shelter from the prevailing winds.

There are also over 20 other localised hedge laying variations to be found throughout the country.

The objective of hedge-laying is to create stock-proof hedges for different types of stock in different physical conditions. The Hedgelaying Association's website says *"Hedges were created to keep animals in fields… . The care of hedges must be concerned with keeping them in the condition to fulfil their original purpose."*

Although it is certainly desirable that hedges should be kept in the condition to fulfil their purpose, it should not be assumed that all hedges have the same purpose or need the same management, or that the purpose is static. It is also worth remembering that stock fences were only one of the historical purposes of hedges.

Welsh style of hedge laying

Hedge laying is labour intensive, and today that means expensive. Unfortunately, therefore, the skills and traditions of hedge management have declined over the last 50 years. This has been largely precipitated by developments in machinery for hedge cutting. Such specialist machinery was first exhibited at the Royal Agricultural Show in 1948. Since then machines have become more sophisticated and quicker which means that the economical way of managing hedges is now by machine.

The disadvantages of machine cutting are that gaps in hedges develop and are not filled and saplings that should be recruited to become the next generation of hedge trees are cut off, while mature hedge trees are regarded as an inconvenience. Indeed it has been stated to the authors that *"hedge trees are a major problem to modern hedge cutters, because they have to take their cutting blades from the hedge and slow their pace of cutting whenever a hedge tree is present."* Flailed saplings could recover if mechanical cutting ceases or is modified, but the new growth would need careful formative pruning for the trees to survive to maturity.

Whether by accident or design, fewer and fewer saplings survive the cutting regime, exacerbating the problems outlined by the Merthyr committee on replacement saplings, and potentially sounding the death-knell for Britain's hedge trees.

However it is not inevitable that the use of mechanical hedge trimmers will result in the loss of hedge trees. With hedge management following some guiding principles the successful combination of a mechanically managed hedge and hedge trees can be achieved.

Guidelines for good hedge trimming [1]

■ Do not cut the hedge every year except
where necessary for safety and security:
eg roadsides, railways, footpaths and
boundaries. As most trees and shrubs in
hedges only produce flowers, nuts and
berries (such as haws and sloes) on year-old
twigs, cutting hedges every year means that
they provide little food for insects, birds
and mammals.

■ Aim to cut hedges on a two or three year
rotation. Where possible, adjacent hedges
should be cut in different years and sections
of shrubs and trees left untrimmed.

■ Leave or plant saplings to grow into hedge
trees at intervals in the hedge, or in field
corners. Provide appropriate protection.
Watch out for any tags that are marking
any new hedge trees (see page 88) to ensure
they are not damaged or destroyed.

■ Cut hedges preferably during January or
February, if ground conditions permit. It is
illegal to cut hedges during the bird nesting
season (mid-March to July) if nests are
being built or if they are being used.

■ Prepare plans of a farm's hedges showing
how frequently they should be cut, and
mark any new hedge trees on them. This
will enable the contractor to know the
cutting regime, allowing the landowner to
make changes if they are required.

These guidelines apply to hedges in a reasonably
good state of growth. However a 'gappy' or
overgrown hedge may need to be coppiced back
to ground level to encourage re-growth.

Although cutting a hedge with three years' growth
may leave it looking badly damaged, occasional
heavy cutting rather than annual trimming is
often better for the hedge and its wildlife.

Mechanical cutting – 5th - 10th year

When cutting a hedge it is preferable not to cut
back to the same point. New shoots will grow just
behind the cut and it is this characteristic
branching that produces dense growth and overall
gains in hedge height and width which are ideal
for stock control and wildlife.

Unfortunately cutting back to the same point
removes new shoots and results in the old shoots
becoming woody, splintered and lacking in vigour.
It can also result in loss of density at the hedge
base. All hedges, except perhaps holly, will
therefore need laying or coppicing eventually
(see page 57), otherwise they will become thin
at the base.

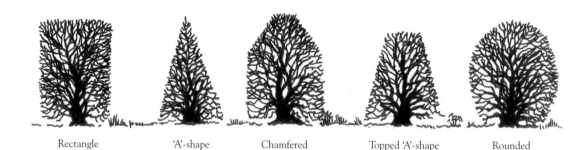

| Rectangle | 'A'-shape | Chamfered | Topped 'A'-shape | Rounded |

HEDGE SHAPES

The shape in which a hedge is cut can have a significant effect on the biodiversity and hedge tree population. It is important therefore to consider the optimum shape for each hedge before cutting.

The 'rectangular' shape is the most frequently seen hedge shape, although the 'A' shape is better for hedge trees and for conservation purposes. In the 'A' shape, the hedge trees can grow through the hedge, whilst its narrow top reduces the hedge's self-shading. The 'A' shape also prevents accumulation of snow and minimises wind turbulence. This shape provides structural diversity at different levels in the hedge, and the wide base provides good cover for many forms of wildlife.

Where space is restricted or where there is rich ground flora at the base, a 'rectangular' shape may be required, however cutting the top off the hedge reduces the chances of hedge trees growing, unless they are carefully cut around.

The 'chamfered' and 'topped A' shape can result in healthy, bulky hedges but they will all need more passes of the flail than the simple 'A' shape.

Finally the 'rounded shape' is often a product of hand trimming, where the trees can be left to grow if required.

COPPICING

One traditional method of reinvigorating hedges is to coppice them. This system involves cutting the hedge back to a series of low stumps which then re-grow. Many broad-leaved tree species, including hazel can be cut down to the stump from which they re-grow; the notable exception being beech. They re-grow producing multiple stems called poles which can be harvested. The hedge can then be cut on a short rotation of between 7 and 15 years to provide small wood, usually for fuel.

Historically in parts of Essex and Suffolk, and probably elsewhere in the country, the timing of hedge coppicing needed to be integrated into the

Coppice method

RIGHT   WRONG

overall management of the farm. During the first years after coppicing the hedge, when the hedge was cut to the ground, the adjacent fields were turned to an arable crop. Then as the hedge re-grew and became or was made stock proof, the land was turned to grass and stock kept in the fields until the next coppicing.

Unfortunately as coppiced hedges are not stock proof for several years after cutting, they need reinforcing, usually using stakes of material taken from the hedge and banged into the ground to fill the gap. Alternatively a newly coppiced hedge can be fenced off to provide effective stock proofing until the hedge re-grows.

In the coppiced hedge the mature trees can be pollarded, as they would have been in a pasture woodland situation. (Under a pasture woodland system the area was usually grazed by domestic animals whilst the trees were treated as pollards or as large timber trees). This therefore makes certain hedges a curious hybrid between the two types of woodland management – coppice and wood-pasture.

HOW TO COPPICE A HEDGE

With a hedge that needs to be coppiced, start by cutting each stem back parallel to and within 7.5 centimetres (3 inches) of the base to form a 'stool'. From the edge of the stool a number of shoots will grow up and these can then be protected and eventually managed by:

- trimming in the early years to produce a dense bushy hedge base

- allowing the poles to grow and then cut again in 7 to 20 years depending on species and location

- allowing the poles to grow for a few years; they can be layed and the hedge allowed to enter a cutting cycle.

Coppicing should be undertaken in the winter months when the sap is not rising.

Coppiced hedge – Years 0 - 5

HEDGE TREES NEAR HIGH VOLTAGE OVERHEAD POWER LINES AND UNDERGROUND SERVICES

HIGH VOLTAGE OVERHEAD POWER LINES

Trees grow, bend and flex in the wind and even occasionally fall over; as a result they can come into contact with the live conductors of an overhead power line. Specified distances (electrical safety clearances) between overhead power lines and obstructions such as trees have been nationally determined to ensure safety to the public and to prevent electrical flashover of the line, which could result in power failures. National Grid Transco regularly undertakes assessments of the likely danger to its system and the public arising from overhead power lines near to trees. Where woody vegetation is found to infringe statutory safety clearances it is cut and/or removed, so that reasonable growth and safe access for future works can be achieved without returning every year to the same site.

National Grid Transco cannot prevent trees and vegetation being planted beneath its overhead power lines since it does not own the land. However to ensure the safety of the public and reliability of its network National Grid Transco recommends that only low height and slow growing species are planted beneath overhead electricity lines. Similarly, when planting is proposed very near pylons, consideration should be given to the need to maintain access to the pylon base to allow overhead line maintenance activities to take place safely with minimum disturbance to established habitats.

The diagram illustrates planting zones beneath and adjacent to a high voltage overhead line where the height of trees and woody vegetation must be restricted to ensure electrical safety clearances can be maintained. The diagram is for illustrative purposes only. The specific clearance available at a particular location and therefore the precise extent of any planting zone will be dependent on the following factors:

- the design of the overhead line and type of pylon
- the operating voltage
- the spacing between pylons
- local topography
- proposals to alter ground levels.

Detailed technical advice together with profile drawings of a specific high voltage overhead line span should be obtained from National Grid Transco prior to any landscaping scheme being finalised.

ZONE CHARACTERISTICS

 Tall – Forest scale trees
e.g. ash, beech, horse chestnut, lime, oak.

 Medium – Garden and orchard scale trees
e.g. apple, cherry, hawthorn, rowan, pear, plum.

 Low
e.g. hedges, allotments, arable crops, reed beds, meadows/wild flowers, grassland.

UNDERGROUND CABLES AND GAS SERVICES

Where there are underground services, it is necessary to keep vegetation away from the power cables and gas pipelines. The route of underground cables and pipelines are shown by markers on the surface. Ideally no woody vegetation should be planted above underground electricity cables. The only hardwood plants which can be planted directly across a gas pipeline are hedge plants such as hawthorn and blackthorn, and even these should only be planted if necessary for screening or for field hedges.

Hedge trees eg ash, beech or oak should not be planted within six metres (18 feet) of the centre of the pipeline, and ideally over 10 metres (33 feet) away.

TREE PLANTING: PROXIMITY TO GAS PIPELINES

Ten metres minimum

Poplar – *Populus sp*
Willow – *Salix sp*

Six metres minimum:
All 'forest' tree species for example

Ash – *Fraxinus excelsior*
Beech – *Fagus sylvatica*
Chestnut – *Aesculus hippocastanum*
Elm – *Ulmus sp*
Lime – *Tilia x europaea*
London plane – *Platanus x hispanica*
Hornbeam – *Carpinus betulus*
Oak – *Quercus sp*
Sweet chestnut – *Castanea sativa*
Sycamore – *Acer pseudoplatanus*
Spruce, Larch, etc

Three metres minimum:
Smaller 'amenity' trees may be planted closer to the pipe. Good ornamental trees including:

Whitebeam – *Sorbus aria*
Swedish whitebeam – *Sorbus intermedia*
Mountain ash or rowan – *Sorbus aucuparia*
False acacia – *Robinia pseudacacia 'Frisia'*
Cockspur thorn – *Crataegus crus-galli*
Hawthorn, Double Scarlet
  – *Crataegus laevigata 'Coccinea Plena'*
Hawthorn, Double Pink
  – *Crataegus laevigata 'Rosea Flore Plena'*
Wild cherry – *Prunus avium*
Ornamental crab apple – *Malus 'Floribunda'*

Shrub under planting – One metre minimum

Guelder rose – *Viburnum opulus*
Dogwood – *Cornus sanguinea*
Sweet Briar – *Rosa rubiginosa*
                Rosa rubrifolia

There are several ways of establishing new
hedge trees:

- selecting existing saplings growing
  in the hedge (see page 88)

- planting trees to fill in existing gaps
  in a hedge

- cutting notches into a hedge and
  planting trees

- planting trees beside a hedge

- planting trees in a new hedge

With all these methods it is important to ensure
that the trees survive when the hedge is cut.
One way to help with this is to tag young trees
to ensure that they are visible to the hedge
cutter (see page 88).

Research has shown that planting new trees in tree
shelters in a hedge is an effective and economical
method of establishing new hedge trees [1].

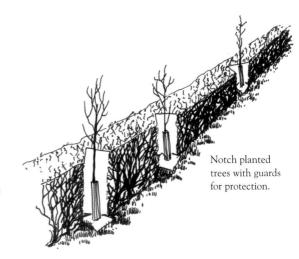

Notch planted
trees with guards
for protection.

A new Welsh hedge planted on top of a
bank, which will eventually provide greater
protection for livestock from the wind.

GAP PLANTING

This involves planting trees into existing gaps in a
hedge. There will be less competition between the
new plants and the hedge plants. Plant the trees
in the centre of the gap to reduce shading and
competition – then plant up the gap around the
tree with new hedging plants if necessary

NOTCH PLANTING

Cut a notch into a hedge and plant a tree as
shown in the diagram. This allows easy tree
planting and weed control. Forestry Commission
experiments showed that, using this technique,
the survival of pedunculate oak (*Quercus robur*)
increased from 20% to 70% after two years when
the trees were kept generally weed free.

PLANTING TREES BESIDE A HEDGE

Another method is to plant trees beside the hedge. This takes up more space, but has the benefit of increasing the hedge width and thus its wildlife value. There will be negligible root competition for water with the hedge itself, although weeds and grass can still be very competitive – so the newly planted trees will need regular weed control. Avoid planting trees on valuable habitats, such as unimproved grassland; in these situations plant trees close to the hedge.

PLANTING TREES IN A NEW HEDGE

When planting a new hedge, it is well worth planning to include some trees which can be allowed to grow to full size. Carried out correctly this is the most effective way to produce new hedge trees.

Select suitable tree species from those shown on pages 74-79. Plant the trees as shown on page 70. It may be worth planting trees that are large enough to be visible above the other hedge plants.

Initially there may be no visible difference between the 'trees' in the hedge and the rest of the hedge plants, unless they are of different species from the rest of the hedge, so it is important to remember the new trees and avoid cutting them. The trees could be marked on hedge plans or tagged and protected from cutting as shown on page 88. Alternatively select the most vigorously growing suitable trees, tag them and mark them on a plan, just before the first cutting.

It may be several years before the trees are big enough to be self sufficient. It is important, therefore, that the plan to develop trees within the hedge is passed on to future managers.

TREE SHELTERS

Tree shelters provide several benefits in hedges as they:

- encourage increased growth rates
- make saplings more visible to hedge managers, ensuring they project well above the top of the new hedge and the current growth
- protect the new trees from grazing animals
- help to stop the hedge swamping the tree
- assist in weed control, if chemicals are to be used

Be sure to revisit tree shelters and carefully pull out any grass and weeds growing inside them.

URBAN HEDGES

Most of the information in this book applies to hedges in rural situations. However, there is no reason why hedge trees cannot be encouraged in urban hedges, using similar techniques. As many urban hedges are cut by hand it should be easier to protect new trees. Issues such as shading or proximity to buildings may be important, but these can be discussed with any interested hedge owner. The easiest place to establish a hedge tree may well be in garden hedges, at a point furthest from buildings.

WHAT SIZE OF YOUNG TREES SHOULD BE PLANTED?

Whips are cheaper, easy to move and usually establish better than larger trees. However, when planting trees into a new hedge it may be worth using trees slightly larger than the adjoining hedge plants.

Transplant	Whip	Feathered 2.2m	Standard 3m	Heavy standard
< 1m	1-1.5m	(roots and stem trimmed)	(roots and stem pruned)	(roots and stem pruned)

SUPPLY OF TREES

Wherever possible, planting stock should be raised from the seed of healthy trees growing on or near the site to be planted (see page 80). Raising trees from seed or stock of local origin helps to ensure the survival of local genetic strains.

If purchasing trees from a nursery, check the origin of each species and be wary if the nursery is unable to supply the information. Some nurseries list the origin of each species in their catalogues. Many nurseries now have a policy of increasing the use of seed from British seed sources.

WHAT TYPE OF TREE
SHOULD BE PURCHASED

Before purchasing any tree check that it is
healthy and undamaged and the roots are moist
and not 'pot-bound'.

There is a variety of forms in which trees are
offered for sale including:

Container-grown: increasingly available as the
container protects the roots and the trees can be
planted at any season. However, they are more
expensive and need good care and may need plenty
of water if the first season after planting is dry.

Bare-rooted: acceptable for most deciduous trees

Root-balled: for evergreen and exotic species

Inspect trees as soon as they arrive and return
them immediately to the nursery if they are in
an unfit condition for planting.

Young rowan trees in a nursery

Bare-root　　　　　Root-balled　　　　　Container

ORDERING NURSERY TREES

Local suppliers of trees may be listed in the Yellow Pages under 'Nurseries-Horticultural' or 'Garden Centres' but most of these will specialise in container-grown ornamental stock. However, many garden centres will supply other types of tree to order. For native trees in quantity the best starting point is to contact the local Wildlife Trust or BTCV office, or even the tree officer at the county or district council, who should be able to provide the names of local suppliers.

For large numbers of trees it is best to place orders as early as possible, by July or August for supply in the late autumn/winter. Lifting of open ground stock will take place when the plants are dormant, usually starting in October/November, depending on the species concerned and the season. If mild weather continues late into the autumn, lifting will have to be delayed. When placing an order, request delivery on a specific date if necessary, but be prepared to be flexible as either mild or very wet weather can affect lifting, just as very cold weather can delay planting.

PRE-PLANTING CARE

Every year thousands of trees are planted which are already dead, due to careless handling

between the time they are lifted from the nursery and final planting-out. Unfortunately these trees are not readily identifiable before they are planted and the first sign of a problem may be when they fail to grow.

It is essential to ensure that:

- bare root trees are delivered with their roots wrapped in plastic

- if not planted immediately, bare-root trees are removed from the bags and heeled–in. For short periods of storage (24 hours or less) bags of trees may be stored in a cool shady position out of the wind

- root-balled and container trees are stored upright, standing on an impervious surface

- as much short fibrous root is kept on the trees as possible

- mechanical damage to the roots is avoided, including breaking the stem tops and stripping the bark from stem or roots

- trees are stored only where there is free drainage, so that the trees do not stand in waterlogged conditions

- the roots are protected from heat.

Trees stored in a bag, in the shade with tops kept free.

Do not store in water.

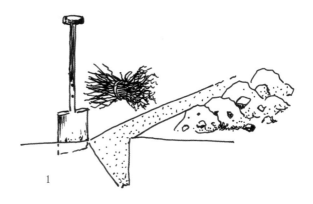

As much fibrous root as possible should
be retained, and avoid damage.

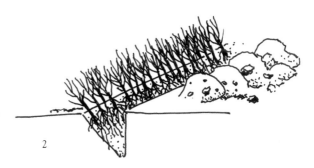

HEELING-IN

Ideally, trees should be lifted, transported and
replanted without interruption. Often, however,
they may need to be stored before planting.
The traditional storage method is to heel-in.

1   Dig a trench in good fresh moist soil which
    will not dry out or become waterlogged.
    Cultivated nursery ground is ideal provided
    it is shaded. Dig the trench with a sloping
    back, deep enough for the trees to be put in
    and their roots completely covered.

2   Trees in bundles should be separated and
    spaced along the trench to keep the trees in
    the centres of the bundles from drying out
    or - in the case of evergreens - from heating
    up. It is convenient to place a marker stick
    every 50 or 100 trees to save counting later.
    Place the trees with their roots completely
    in the trench but with their tops out.

3   Place soil over the roots to cover them
    and lightly firm the soil around the roots
    by treading.

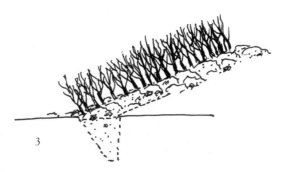

Plant trees at any time over the season from October to March or April but avoid planting on days when the ground is frozen. A good time to plant is during the Tree Council's National Tree Week, from the last weekend in November until the first weekend in December.

Hard frost is most likely in January and February. Plant half-hardy species (suitable only for western coastal districts) in spring.

Deciduous trees are best planted before Christmas. They will survive spring planting but are more likely to suffer from drought than if planted in the autumn or early winter.

Evergreens are best planted either early or late in the planting season. Spring planting should take place when the soil has begun to warm and the first flush of new growth occurs.

In dry areas late autumn planting is best for most species, to give the trees a chance to become established before spring droughts. In wet areas, early spring planting is generally best. Ideally the site should be drained to get rid of excess water.

Where soils are wet and then freeze there is a risk of 'frost lift' which can be devastating for newly planted trees. However this is unlikely in most years, especially where there is protection from a hedge.

Whenever the trees are planted the roots should be shaded, cool and damp. Be sure to firm-in trees by treading in well.

Although container-grown trees can be planted at any time of year, the preceding guidelines will give best results for them too. If planting is done in late spring or summer, container-grown trees should be watered during dry spells for the first growing season.

THE TREE PLANTING HOLE

Pit planting will ensure plenty of room for the new tree's roots, giving the tree the best possible start in a hedge. In good quality soil, dig a hole big enough for all the roots to be spread out. In poor soil, dig a hole wider and deeper than needed to accommodate the roots and partly refill it with the

removed soil. Before refilling, break up the compacted soil around and in the hole, to improve drainage and aeration of the roots.

Continue filling around the roots, treading more firmly until the hole is over-filled, leaving the soil slightly above the surrounding ground. Treading in is most important when pit planting. Many failures are due to lack of firming. In heavy soils do not firm so much that the soil becomes compacted.

Finally, clear grass and weeds for an area of 1 metre (3 feet) diameter around the tree.

SUPPORTS

Stakes and other supports are now only considered necessary for trees which are more than 1 metre (3 feet) tall and only for their first year. After this, well planted trees should no longer need support.

If a stake is necessary attach the tree to it using a flexible tie which will stretch as the tree grows. Loosen or remove the tie if it appears to be strangling the tree at any time.

Tree shelters are intended to stop animals – from mice and rabbits to deer, sheep, cattle and horses – damaging young trees by eating the leaves or stripping the bark. Check the shelters in spring and autumn to ensure they are effective (no bark missing or twigs bitten or broken off) and not rubbing or cutting into the tree.

- If a shelter is not fulfilling its purpose, add more protection, e.g. a taller tree shelter to protect against deer, or fencing to keep off cows and other animals.

- Replace/repair damaged shelters.

- If a shelter is damaging the tree, adjust, modify or replace it.

- If the threat no longer exists because the tree has grown or circumstances have changed remove the shelter so that there is no risk of damage to the tree.

A National Tree Week planting event in Hampshire (left).

Planting a container grown aspen tree in a hedge gap.

69

TWELVE STEPS TO PLANT HEDGE TREES

1 Soak the roots with water for a few hours before planting

2 Dig a hole for the tree that is large enough to allow the tree roots to be spread out

3 Prune out any damaged twigs

4 Remove any containers, and if necessary tease out any 'pot -bound' roots and remove any damaged ones

Moisten roots (but do not wash all the soil off).

5 When planting bare-root trees, space the roots out carefully, having made the hole big enough to avoid bending any roots

6 Carefully hold the tree upright in the middle of the hole, while putting soil over the roots in thin layers

7 Insert a stake into the hole if required (not needed for trees less than 1metre [3 feet] tall) ensuring no roots are damaged

8 Shake the tree gently up and down, so that the soil gets between and around the roots, and firm the soil with your foot

Dig hole, removing roots and rubbish (not more than half a day before planting).

9 Continue filling around the roots, treading more firmly until the hole is over-filled, leaving the soil slightly above the surrounding ground. Ensure that when planting is completed the root collar will be level with the ground surface

10 If support is being used, secure the tree to the support with a flexible tie

11 If the soil is dry, water well

12 Apply mulch (bark or composted woody material, a mulch mat or cut up squares of carpet). Add an adequate shelter if there is a risk of damage from animals or machines

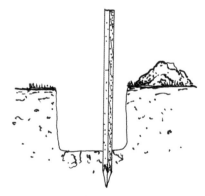

Insert stake (if necessary).

Mix organic material or soil improver,
with spoil, if required.

Fill hole and firm up.

Root and shoot prune.

Fix tie, mulch mat, mulch, guard
(and label) and water in.

Part fill hole, position plant with root collar
level with surface of ground.

When the tree has been planted in its permanent position in the hedge, there is still a range of tasks that need to be undertaken to ensure its survival.

Research has shown that 50% of newly planted trees die in the first five years, due in part to a lack of aftercare. The Tree Council has therefore developed the TLC Campaign, to highlight the three simple tasks that need to be undertaken at least once a year for the first five years to ensure that the young tree survives and thrives. TLC for young hedge trees involves:

- Tending, such as checking shelters and carrying out essential pruning to remove broken and dead branches

- Loosening ties and checking stakes, and

- Clearing all weeds and grasses, ideally from one metre square (3 feet square) around the base of each tree, and applying mulch

TENDING

Check the tree in March or April.

- Is it alive? If there are no leaves, look for green under the bark of twigs (scrape the surface with a fingernail or knife) and living buds

- Fill in any gaps in the soil around the roots and use a foot to firm the new soil. Also firm soil around any trees that may have been lifted by frost

- If the soil is waterlogged, channel the excess away from the tree

- Look for pests and diseases. Changing threats can result from changes in land use

- If the tree is dead, try to work out why and correct the problem (seeking advice if necessary) so that when a new tree is planted it does not suffer the same fate.

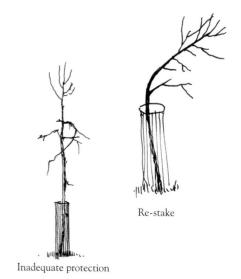

Re-stake

Inadequate protection

Re-stake

Pull back up, firm in and re-stake

Re-bury mulch mat

Drain

Formative pruning needed

Reduce crown

Re-stake or loosen tie

Remove tie and stake

Weed problem

Clear weeds to
relieve suppression

PRUNING

Careful formative pruning can prevent problems
in later life. If a tree has two competing upright
shoots, removing one at an early stage to leave
a single main shoot can save the tree from
possible major branch failure in years to come.
Also, cut off any dead branches to minimise the
risk from disease.

LOOSENING

Check the stake and the tie. A young tree should
only need a stake for a year, until its roots have
grown into undisturbed soil to give it stability.

- Is the tie too tight? The tree stem
  should not be under pressure from the
  tie. The tree should not be able to rub
  on the stake or tree shelter

- Does the tree still need a stake? Check
  this in spring by releasing the tie and if
  the tree stays upright, remove the stake

- If the tree leans and the roots move,
  re-tie it to a shortened stake

- If the tree is top heavy and bends over,
  shorten the stake (to just above the
  bend) and replace the tie at the top
  of the stake, to ensure the stem stands
  upright

CLEARING

Pull up or hoe any grass and weeds for a radius
of at least 0.5 metres (1.5 feet). When the soil
is moist early in the year, cover the cleared area
with a mulch mat, bark or brushwood chippings,
or an old piece of carpet. This helps retain
moisture near the roots and reduces competition
from weeds and removes the need for damaging
grass-cutting machinery to be anywhere near
the tree.

COMMON HEDGE TREE SPECIES

When growing new hedge trees, try to copy nature whenever possible by selecting trees already successful on or near the hedge. The following descriptions are of native trees commonly found in British hedges.

ASH – *Fraxinus excelsior*

Ash is a very widespread woodland and hedge native tree growing throughout Britain, preferring moist, but well-drained and fertile calcareous soils. Large, spreading ash trees can often be seen in hedges and a mature ash can produce 100,000 seeds (keys), which can go on to produce more hedge trees.

Its strong wood is flexible and was used as an element in wheel making, for skis, oars and tool handles. It is still used for high-quality furniture.

It is a species with a high wildlife value. Pockets of decayed wood in the trunk and branches are used as a nesting site by woodpeckers and other hole-nesters, including redstarts (*Phoenicurus phoenicurus*) and bats. The tree also supports up to 68 species of invertebrates and over 200 species of lichen throughout its range.

The leaves of the ash have 9 to 13 pairs of stalked leaflets with a single terminal leaflet. The single seeds have a long wing.

The leaves of English oak are almost stalkless and the acorns have long stalks, whilst the leaves of Sessile oak (above) have distinct stalks, and the acorns are without stalks, hence the name 'sessile' (unstalked).

ENGLISH OAK – *Quercus robur*
AND SESSILE OAK – *Quercus petraea*

There are two native oak species in Britain, the English oak being a tree of woodlands, hedges and parkland in many parts of Britain, while the Sessile is largely restricted to woodlands and hedges in the west of Britain. Where the two species meet they may hybridise.

The English oak grows best on deep fertile clays and loams but will tolerate a wide range of soils. The sessile oak prefers areas of high rainfall and grows best in deep, well-drained clays and loams. Some of the largest oaks in Britain, of both species, are thought to be over 1,000 years old.

Throughout its natural range English oak supports 500 species of invertebrates, more than any other species of British tree, although the sessile also supports large numbers of insects. Cavities in oaks are used by birds and bats as roosting and nesting sites. Their hard durable timber is used for boats, buildings, fencing and furniture.

Oaks are often seen as the quintessential British landscape tree, and have often been used as a boundary marker in hedges in the past because of their durability and longevity.

FIELD MAPLE – *Acer campestre*

Britain's only native maple, the field maple is a species which prefers lime-rich soil, but will tolerate other conditions. It occurs naturally in hedges and as the understorey in woods and copses throughout England and Wales. In the past, it was used for topiary.

The wood of the field maple is soft but produces beautiful veneer, used for wood turning and furniture. Historically, it was also used to make harps.

It is an important habitat for up to 51 invertebrate species, the plumed prominent moth (*Ptilophora plumigera*) being the most characteristic of these. The fruit 'keys' are often eaten by small mammals. It provides excellent autumn colour.

The leaves of hazel are soft and hairy and have saw-toothed edges with a drawn-out tip. The nuts grow in clusters of up to four each, enclosed by a leafy structure known as a 'bract'.

HAZEL – *Corylus avellana*

Hazel is found throughout Britain, growing in woods and hedges on a wide range of soils, including chalk and limestone, mildly acid soils, and clays. The male catkins often appear in January or February, adding the first splash of colour to the winter woodlands.

Hazel is usually coppiced to produce thin flexible poles which are used for fencing, hurdles, pea and bean sticks and thatching spars.

Coppiced hazel hedges are rich in wildlife, as the regular cutting allows light to reach the hedge floor, which benefits flowers and butterflies. Over 106 invertebrate species have been found on this tree throughout its range. Mammals feed on the hazelnuts, which are particularly attractive to squirrels and dormice.

The small leaves of field maple have three main lobes and two smaller basal lobes. Each pair of seeds lies almost in a straight line, and may have pink tinges.

BEECH – *Fagus sylvatica*

Beech is the dominant native species on chalk and limestone. It prefers well-drained soils but can be found in heavy clays. It has been widely planted in parks and gardens, often as a single species hedge. Beech can retain its leaves through most of the winter, which is one of the reasons it is favoured for hedging. However mature trees do not retain their leaves. The world's tallest hedge is also of beech, at Meikleour in Perthshire.

The wood is strong and tough, was used for tool handles and flooring and is still widely used for kitchen utensils and children's toys. The beech mast (nuts) has been used as pig feed.

Middle aged trees are susceptible to bark stripping by grey squirrels (*Sciurus carolinensis*). This can lead to crown dieback and deformed crowns.

Some 94 species of invertebrates have been found in beech throughout its range, including the lobster (*Stauropus fagi*) and barred hooked-tip moths (*Drepana cultraria*).

Beech has oval leaves with a wavy margin. The seeds are contained in a brown husk.

Shiny evergreen leaves of holly have a waxy upperside and spiny edges. Trees are either male or female.

HOLLY – *Ilex aquifolium*

Holly is a widespread native tree which grows on almost any soil. It tolerates shade well, often growing as the understorey in woodlands but also likes open situations and occurs widely in hedges. In Sussex and Herefordshire, holly planted in hedges was said to prevent witches from running over their tops.

It is one of the few native evergreen trees, and an important source of berries for thrushes in winter. Only females have berries, but males are needed nearby before the females can produce berries. Despite the prickly leaves holly can still be grazed by livestock and deer, and in the past was used as fodder.

Its hard, white wood takes stain well and was traditionally known as 'English Ebony'. It was particularly used for carving and inlay, whilst the shoots with berries are still used for Christmas decorations.

Holly is the food plant of the holly blue butterfly (*Celastrina argiolus*) but only nine other invertebrate species have been found feeding on this tree throughout its wide natural distribution.

HAWTHORN – *Crataegus monogyna*

Hawthorn grows throughout Britain, except in the extreme north west of Scotland. It tolerates most soils except peat and is one of the commonest hedge shrubs. Here it is usually clipped into shape, but the species can grow into a distinctive small tree if left unmanaged.

The wood has been used for tool handles and walking sticks and also produces excellent firewood and charcoal. The berries can be made into jellies, chutneys and wine.

The species has a high wildlife value, as its 'May' flowers provide nectar for spring insects and its berries provide excellent food for small mammals and birds, especially thrushes. Over 209 invertebrate species have been recorded living on this tree throughout its range.

The leaves of hawthorn (above) have deeply divided lobes. The fleshy red berries (haws) contain a single seed.

Each leaf of the rowan consists of our or more pairs of stalkless leaflets. It has distinctive red berries.

ROWAN – *Sorbus aucuparia*

Rowan is found throughout Britain, growing naturally at altitudes of up to 1,000 metres (3000 feet) in Scotland. It is a tree of mountains, woodlands and valleys, growing on a wide range of soils including chalks, acid soils and even peat.

Its timber is strong, hard and flexible, leading to its use in tools, carving and for shortbows, which were favoured mainly by the Welsh. The berries can be turned into a jelly, said to be excellent with cold game or wildfowl, and a wholesome 'perry' or cider can also be made from them.

The tree has excellent wildlife values, providing fruit for thrushes and blackbirds, which help to disperse the seed around the countryside. Berries and leaves provide good autumn colour.

Other hedge trees include: bird cherry (left), crabapple (middle) and black poplar (bottom).

The previous five pages show the most common hedge trees. However, many other species do occur, some of which are shown here.

ELM – *Ulmus species*

Elm is still an important hedge tree, but it rarely survives beyond about 15 years old, when it becomes vulnerable to the beetles which carry the Dutch elm disease fungus.

SYCAMORE – *Acer pseudoplatanus*

Sycamore is non-native but grows in exposed and difficult sites where other trees cannot survive. It supports a large volume of insects which provide good bird food. A very significant component of the north of England and Scottish landscapes.

WILLOW – *Salix species*

Willows like wet and boggy areas. They are an important early spring nectar source for butterflies and other insects. Their brittle wood and usually short life often results in the tree collapsing, so they are best grown away from roads. These trees are frequently pollarded.

FRUIT TREES

Apple – *Malus sylvestris*, Pear – *Pyrus communis*, Cherry – *Prunus padus* and *P. avium*

There are many fruit trees which make good hedge trees, providing fruit for birds and people.

Other native hedge trees include: alder, birch, blackthorn, damson, hornbeam, lime, native poplars, whitebeam, yew.

Seeds collected from hedge trees can be a source of free trees for growing on and replanting. The Tree Council and its members promote an annual initiative called Seed Gathering Sunday on the second Sunday in October, to encourage the growing of trees from seed.

Here is a summary of how to collect seeds and grow on new trees for the future – full details are given in the Good Seed Guide, available from the Tree Council for £3.50 inc p&p. There is also information on the Tree Council website (**www.treecouncil.org.uk**), on the Seed Gathering Sunday pages.

Do not collect the first seeds to fall from a tree, as later seed will probably be of better quality. Watch carefully as your seed ripens, for delaying too long may mean the squirrels and other animals beat you to it. However, always leave some seeds, as they are an important food source for wildlife.

Climbing trees is dangerous, so only collect seed you can reach from the ground. Use gloves if you are collecting seed from spiny trees or bushes. If you want to collect seed from the lower branches of trees, pick them by hand or use a hooked stick to carefully pull branches down to within your reach.

SEED COLLECTING

Very few trees produce good crops of seed every year. Keep an eye on the quality and quantity of seed developing on the trees. Check that seeds are ripe before you collect them.

When ripe, the seeds should be picked directly from the tree, or gathered from the ground. Use a paper or cloth bag to take your seeds home. Do not use plastic bags as they may cause the seeds to sweat and become mouldy, which will reduce their chances of germination. Put seeds from different species of trees in separate bags and label them.

Ideally seeds should be collected from trees that are growing well in your area and are obviously suited to local conditions. If the trees are on private land, it is very important to get the permission of the landowner.

SEED PREPARATION

Most tree seeds are contained in some kind of
fruit – apple pips are a good example – and the
seeds will first need to be extracted and cleaned.
You will never get all of your seeds to germinate,
but by using the following methods your chances
of success can be greatly increased.

The method you should use depends on the type
of fruit or seed you have collected – nuts, fleshy
fruits, winged seeds or cones.

Once you have separated your seeds into types,
you will know from this page whether they need
to be either stratified for the winter (see page 84),
or sown immediately into pots or seedbeds.

FLESHY FRUITS: eg holly, yew,
hawthorn, whitebeam, rowan, cherry,
blackthorn, buckthorn, elder, apple and pear

Mix the berries with water and then gently mash them with a potato masher or similar
device. Viable seed will sink to the bottom and the residue of the fleshy fruit can be
discarded. For rowan put the berries in a sieve and gently squeeze them with your fingers
under running water to release the seeds. The seeds of all fleshy fruits need to be stratified.

CONES: eg pine, alder and birch

Put the ripe cones in a paper bag to dry out
naturally for a few days – but not in direct
sunlight, on a radiator or by a fire. The cones
will open up and release their seeds which are
then ready to be sown.

NUTS: eg oak, beech and hazel

Separate the nuts from their outer casings or cups, but leave the shells undamaged, and drop them into a bucket or bowl of water. Discard the ones that float and collect those that sink for sowing. Beech and hazel nuts should be stratified (see page 84) and then sown when they have germinated.

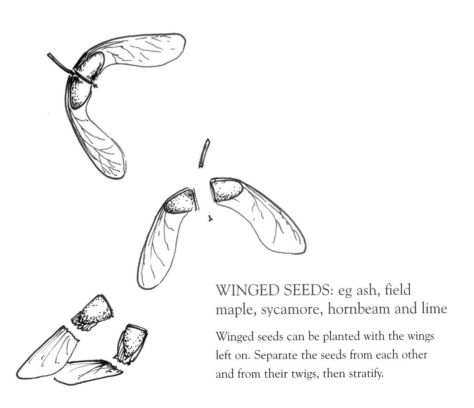

WINGED SEEDS: eg ash, field maple, sycamore, hornbeam and lime

Winged seeds can be planted with the wings left on. Separate the seeds from each other and from their twigs, then stratify.

SEED STRATIFICATION AND GERMINATION

Very few tree seeds will grow without exposure to the cold of at least one winter. Other species take even longer, needing the following summer plus another winter before showing signs of life. This is because of a natural defence mechanism built into the seeds, which ensures that they do not grow during the winter months when the young seedlings might be killed by the cold.

Tree growers have developed a technique called **stratification** which aims to mimic this natural process. To stratify your seeds, mix them with a stratification medium (see caption for recipe) and put them in a pot or bucket which has holes in the bottom for drainage.

The mixture must be kept just moist but not saturated. It is moist enough if you can squeeze out a drop of water when you pinch the mixture between your thumb and forefinger.

In the spring, tip out the mixture and remove any seeds that are showing small shoots or roots. These seeds are germinating and are ready for sowing. Any seeds that have not germinated should be put back into the stratification mixture. Keep checking the seeds weekly during the spring, sowing any that germinate.

Once the seeds are growing, it is important to sow them quickly, as the new trees are fragile. If they get too large, they can be damaged during planting.

If any seeds have not germinated by the end of the spring, do not be disheartened. It is possible they may need two winters, but check that the seeds have not rotted before continuing to stratify.

Tree leaves and fruits, from the top: field maple, hazel, lime, sweet chestnut and rowan.

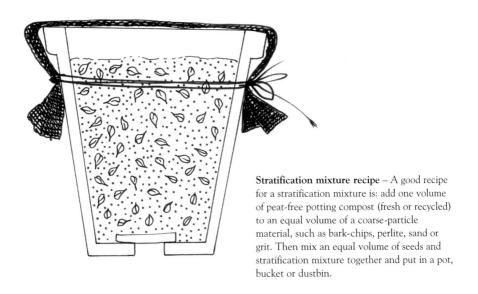

Stratification mixture recipe – A good recipe for a stratification mixture is: add one volume of peat-free potting compost (fresh or recycled) to an equal volume of a coarse-particle material, such as bark-chips, perlite, sand or grit. Then mix an equal volume of seeds and stratification mixture together and put in a pot, bucket or dustbin.

Containers – Use whatever size containers you have to hand. The most important thing is to ensure that the tops are covered with wire mesh to prevent animals from eating the seeds. Then bury them in the ground, place against a north-facing wall or keep in a cool outhouse.

Once you have prepared and, if necessary, stratified your seeds they are ready for sowing. Sow your seeds in a suitable container – such as a milk carton or 'Rootrainer' – or in an outdoor seedbed.

Small seeds like birch and alder should be sown on the surface of the compost or soil and covered with a thin layer of sharp sand. It is best to sow several small seeds (a pinch) in each container and then thin to leave the strongest seedlings. Larger seeds are usually sown singly and covered to about one-and-a half times their average length.

Wherever you sow your seeds, you will need to ensure that they do not become waterlogged. In containers, this can be achieved by ensuring that there are holes in the bottom. In outdoor seedbeds, digging in some sand and grit may help improve the drainage of heavy soils.

Germinating seeds will need shelter from hot sun, cold winds, frost, birds, mice and other animals. A shady spot against a wall is ideal. Make sure you water your containers regularly, especially in the summer. Occasionally give the seedlings some liquid plant feed especially if the trees are held over into a second year. Weed the containers, but make sure you avoid pulling up the young trees by mistake.

MOVING SAPLINGS

Another option is to search for seedlings growing in unsuitable places, such as fields that will be ploughed. These can be carefully dug up, keeping as much soil around the roots as possible, then either grown-on in a tree nursery or planted into the hedge as described on page 62.

PLANTING OUT

Once the seedlings have grown to a suitable size for planting in a hedge, follow the planting ideas outlined on page 62.

Small seeds like birch and alder should be sown on the surface of the compost or soil and covered with a thin layer of sharp sand

Larger seeds are usually sown singly and covered to about one-and-a half times their average length

MILK CARTON

This is an ideal method for growing a single tree. First, cut off the top of your milk or juice carton and then pierce small holes in the bottom to allow water to escape. Fill it with potting compost (preferably peat-free) and sow either a single germinating seed, or a pinch of small seeds. As the tree grows, water regularly to ensure the compost does not dry out. After a few months the young tree may outgrow its carton, so the tree should be transferred to a larger container or planted out.

ROOTRAINER

'Rootrainers' are small moulded plastic cells which come in hinged packs with four or five cells in each row, allowing you to open them up to examine how your young trees are developing. Five or six rows of 'Rootrainer' packs can be placed together in a tray, allowing 20 or more trees to be grown in a small space.

As with milk cartons, fill with potting compost (preferably peat-free) and sow either a single germinating seed, or a pinch of small seeds, in each one. As the trees grow, water regularly. When the young trees have grown well-developed roots, they are ready to be planted out. ('Rootrainers' can be obtained from most garden centres and shops or from specialised stockists.)

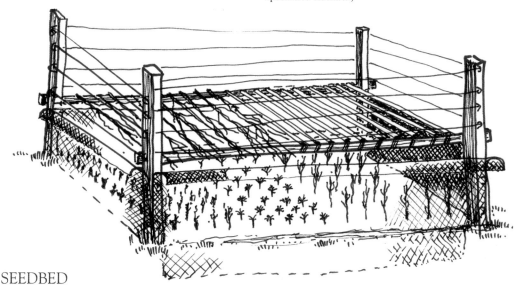

SEEDBED

A seedbed is a mini tree-nursery. To create a seedbed, first prepare the soil to ensure that it is free draining and if necessary add some coarse grit to improve drainage. Either sow your seeds on the surface of the seedbed or in small trenches, before covering them with a layer of soil.

Use a protective fence to keep rabbits and rodents away from your seeds and seedlings. As the young trees grow, ensure they are watered regularly. Trees growing in seed beds can be left for a year or more before being planted out.

TAGGING EXISTING HEDGE TREES

Tagging hedge trees with brightly coloured tags is a simple way to alert hedge cutters, enabling them to avoid the trees. If done correctly it will add new trees to the countryside, and will benefit landowners by adding to their future stock of trees, with all their many uses. Tagging could also be used in urban areas, parks and gardens. In all cases permission must be obtained from the owner.

Tagging is an important way of protecting trees which have been newly planted into a hedge.

As part of its Hedge Tree Campaign, launched in 2003, the Tree Council is encouraging its 7500 Tree Wardens, and many other supporters and member organisations, to tag trees. This is a revival of an earlier Tree Council tagging scheme, which was very successful in the 1980s.

The tag will only work if the hedge cutters are asked to avoid the tagged trees (see below).

GETTING PERMISSION

It is essential to approach farmers and landowners for permission to go on the land before starting tagging, and to get their support. A good first step may be to contact the local Farming and Wildlife Advisory Group (FWAG) or National Farmers Union (NFU) representatives to ask about farmers who may be interested in your area. Alternatively ask locally about who may own hedges which look suitable, and contact them. If necessary local ownership records could be examined at the Land Registry.

A fine example of a young hedge tree that would be worth tagging.

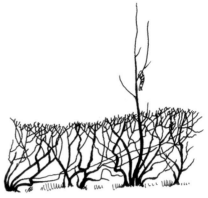

Tagging a new hedge tree; before and after hedge trimming.

Discuss the merits of hedge trees and tagging with the landowners, asking them to suggest suitable hedges and to ensure that hedge-cutters are told to avoid the tagged trees. Find out what they envisage for the landscape. Discuss how many trees it is appropriate to tag. Respect their wishes if they do not want to take part.

If possible show the landowner and hedge cutter the trees you have tagged, and mark them on a map, to help cutters avoid them.

WHAT TO SELECT

When looking for existing saplings it is important that the right type is chosen. The ideal is a young vigorous seedling growing straight up from the hedge base, perhaps resulting from a seed deposited in the hedge. This should produce a good straight trunk, if protected from cutting. With very young seedlings it may be a good idea to help them to become established using a tree shelter (see page 63).

Many hedges will not contain suitable saplings, particularly dense single-species hawthorn and blackthorn hedges. Here it may be better to look for hedge gaps which can be planted up. It is better to choose a small number of good saplings than a large number of variable quality.

The choice of saplings will vary in different hedges. Look for species from page 74 to 79.

In hedges dominated by hawthorn and blackthorn these species will be laid and/or cut regularly, so the hedge will normally be too damaged to produce new trees; here consider planting trees into the hedge

Trees grown from stems that have been flailed, laid or coppiced will be damaged at the point at which they were cut. As they grow the new shoots may develop decay at the junction with the parent plant as a result of the early management. This may result in problems with the mature tree, which may lose limbs.

The best choice of saplings will usually be from a mixed, well-grown hedge that has not been trimmed for two or three years. Any promising saplings will be lost when cutting takes place. As a general rule the oldest hedges have the greatest variety of species and may often be the best source of new tree stocks. It is often difficult to find suitable saplings in close-clipped hawthorn hedges.

Hedges trimmed to an A-shape are probably the most likely mechanically cut hedges to contain suitable saplings, which will be in the tallest part towards the centre of the hedge. While hand trimming a hedge it should be easy for the operator to choose strong saplings and when laying a hedge there may also be a good choice of new saplings.

The best saplings have a single straight stem to the ground. Where one is not available, choose a straight coppice shoot from the strongest root stock.

WHERE TO SELECT

Saplings should be at least 20 metres (60 feet) apart, to allow them to develop into large trees in the future without competing or producing too much shade. Many farmers will want them to be even further apart (over 100 metres, 300 feet), as mechanical cutters find it hard to work between trees that are too close together. An exception to this spacing would be if the landowner wanted to create a small copse of hedge trees closer together, perhaps at a field corner. It is important that they should not be too near overhead services (see page 58), such as power lines, or their branches may cause problems in the future. They should be well back from public roads and tracks used by wide machines, or they risk being damaged or becoming an obstruction.

Selecting several new saplings each year will produce a more balanced age structure for the new trees.

In some situations, small groups of stems can be chosen, either to grow on as a group, or with a view to selecting the strongest sapling the following year, cutting back the others. This can be particularly appropriate for field corners.

Trees in hedges running north to south will produce less crop shading and can provide shelter from prevailing south westerly winds. Avoid shading ponds. However shade can be beneficial for grazing animals, farm buildings and for hot tractor drivers.

WHEN TO SELECT

Once permission has been obtained, tagging can be done at any time before the hedges are cut, which is normally in autumn/winter when there is less other farm work to do.

Trees are easier to identify when they are in leaf. As summer advances hedges and their surrounding field margins can become more overgrown and harder to reach. Also tags placed early in the year may become hidden later, so late summer or autumn is often the best time to tag. Recently cut hedges should be left for two years or more, to allow time for new saplings to become established.

Hedges can support many nesting birds. It is illegal to disturb them in spring.

SAFETY

Always work in pairs, particularly with tall and overgrown hedges and ditches. If working beside a road take extra care; wearing fluorescent clothing greatly increases your visibility to drivers.

PRACTICAL TIPS

- Hand-trim the hedge for about 1 metre (3 feet) on each side of the sapling to make it more visible, or ask the operator of the hedge-cutter to leave an area around the sapling to be hand-trimmed later

- Tie a brightly coloured tag, such as those produced by the Tree Council, around a side shoot or the main stem

- Reaching your chosen saplings can be difficult; strong gloves, coat and boots are recommended as protection. Step ladders may be necessary for tall hedges; always have help when using steps and avoid doing anything which could result in your being hurt

- If it is too hard to reach the chosen tree, consider putting a tagged stick or cane into the ground or the hedge beside the tree. If the marker is temporary, do this just before the hedge cutting starts

- For further protection consider putting a permanent strong, clearly visible stake into the hedge, on either side or adjacent to the chosen tree

- Think about the need for protection from cattle and other animals, rabbits and mice and voles

- Keep a note of which trees you tag. Revisit them annually to replace the tags if necessary, and record survival rates. This information will enable the Tree Council to monitor the success of the Hedge Tree Campaign

- Remove tags and markers once the hedge has been cut

MANAGEMENT

In following years the saplings will have grown above the hedge, but hedge-cutters will need reminding to avoid them. Check the saplings each year, hand trimming around them and renewing tags.

The ancient trees of Britain are increasingly recognised as some of the most important features of our countryside (see page 28). Many of these special old trees are in hedges, where they have been managed for firewood and timber, particularly by pollarding (the regular removal of branches above the height where animals can graze new shoots). Nowadays this is a rare practice, but one which can help produce impressive trees for the future.

The ideal situation is where there are already a good number of hedge trees, so that the owner can afford to reduce the size of some by pollarding. Another opportunity will be when there is a need to limit the size of trees, for example when they are growing under overhead power lines.

The technique can be applied to all young trees but conifers other than yews may respond poorly. All pollards benefit from the retention of side branches but beech and hornbeam may not be successful without these. For this reason it is best to select trees that have plenty of low 'whiskery' branches.

Pollards should be created when the stem is as thick as a broomstick. Older trees have a lower success rate, and the outcome depends to a large extent on species, form and vitality. Additionally, working on large trees requires professional expertise.

New pollards can be created in any situation (apart from in shade). To create a pollard in a hedge, select a suitable tree, then decide on the height at which to cut. This should be high enough to be out of reach of browsing animals, but not so high that working on it becomes dangerous. This is not always achievable. The tree could be cut to hedge height, but would then need to be marked for several years to allow the new growth to develop. This would also give a low new crown which, in addition to interfering with future hedge maintenance, would tend to shade the hedge and cause it to become 'gappy'. There are good reasons why pollards were usually cut at above 2 metres or often around 3 metres.

Tag the tree if there is a danger of it being lost to hedge cutters.

Carry out the pollarding in winter, ideally between January and March, before the leaves emerge. Avoid frosty weather. Remove the upper trunk with a clean cut, angled to allow water to run off. Retain some branches beneath the cut if possible. The cut branches may have a value as fencing material, or for more creative uses such as basket making or willow sculpture. Once a tree has been pollarded it is important to establish a cutting regime (usually 7 to 15 years) to keep it healthy.

It is particularly valuable to re-cut pollards which have been neglected, by removing branches growing out from the previous cut. If this is not done the trees can split apart. If branches are small (4 centimetres in diameter, up to 1.5 inches) it should be possible to remove all of them. If they are larger than this the tree may suffer if all branches are cut, and it may be better to leave some for a year or more until new re-growth has become established. To re-pollard ancient trees, see "Veteran Trees: A guide to good management" [1].

Pollards should be created when the stem is as thick as a broomstick. Older trees have a lower success rate.

Re-pollarding mature trees is valuable, increasing the longevity of certain trees, but needs specials skills.

THE TREE COUNCIL — MAKING TREES MATTER

The Tree Council was founded in 1974 when elms, for centuries a familiar sight in Britain's hedges, were dying in their thousands from Dutch elm disease. This was particularly poignant at a time when more and more hedges and their trees were being removed.

It was launched – as a partnership of organisations working together for trees – to keep up the momentum of National Tree Planting Year, a government initiative with the slogan 'Plant a Tree in '73'. This special year was a countrywide response to the dramatic loss of elms and it resulted in thousands of new trees being planted in communities throughout the UK. The campaign was so successful that it was clear that a new organisation was needed to keep up the momentum.

The Tree Council started as a group of just 20 organisations. Today it is the UK's lead tree campaigning partnership, with 150 member organisations including professional, non-governmental, specialist and trade organisations, as well as other conservation charities, local authorities and government bodies.

It is a registered charity dedicated to inspiring, initiating and enabling effective action for trees in town and countryside. It campaigns to make more people aware that trees matter – and that effective action for trees and woods means a great deal more than just planting new ones. It also works towards more trees, of the right kind and in the right place, and better care for all trees, of all ages.

One of the Tree Council's first acts was to organise National Tree Week, starting in 1975. Now up to a million trees are planted each year as a result of this annual winter festival. These new trees increasingly include elms, being put back into a landscape of which they were once such a characteristic part.

Over the years the Tree Council has launched other major public involvement campaigns, such as Trees Love Care, Walk in the Woods and Seed Gathering Sunday. In 1990, the Tree Council established a nationwide Tree Warden Scheme. This network of 7500 volunteers, who champion local trees in communities throughout the country, is run in partnership with National Grid Transco and is key to the success of the Hedge Tree Campaign.

For further information visit
www.treecouncil.org.uk

National Grid Transco is one of the world's largest utilities and the largest investor owned utility company in the UK. In the UK, through National Grid Company, it owns, operates and develops the high voltage transmission system in England and Wales and through Transco it owns, operates and develops Britain's natural gas transmission and distribution systems. Safety is one of the National Grid Transco's highest priorities and in the interests of safety and system security, it has to ensure that statutory safety clearances are maintained between trees and other vegetation and its network of overhead power lines, underground cables and gas pipelines. Therefore, effective tree management forms a large and vital part of the maintenance programme of these vital energy networks.

The company has worked in partnership with the Tree Council for over 10 years and since 1997, the Tree Warden Scheme has been the focal point of this partnership, providing support for Tree Wardens around the country, to conserve and enhance trees and woodlands and encourage local communities to play an active role. The expert advice National Grid Transco receives from the Tree Council, together with the support of Tree Wardens, is vital in helping the company to manage trees in a safe and sustainable way.

For further information visit
www.ngtgroup.com

THE VALUE OF HEDGES AND HEDGE TREES

1 *The Gardeners Dictionary Vol III.* Miller, P. London 1741

WHAT IS A HEDGE TREE

1 *The Hedgerows Regulations 1997.* Statutory Instrument 1997 No. 1160. HMSO 1997

2 *Hedgerow Survey Handbook.* Bickmore, C. Countryside Council for Wales 2002

3 *Hedges Habitat Action Plan.* West Sussex County Council 2004

4 *Hedgerow Survey Handbook.* Bickmore, C. Countryside Council for Wales 2002

HOW HEDGES HAVE ARISEN

1 *Hedges and Walls.* Williamson, T. National Trust 2002

2 *New Hedges for the Countryside.* Maclean, M. Farming Press 1992

DATING A HEDGE

1 *Hedges.* Pollard, E., Hooper, M., and Moore, N. New Naturalist, Collins 1974

2 *The Gardeners Dictionary Vol II.:* Miller, P. London 1741

3 *Hedges and Walls.* Williamson, T. National Trust 2002

BRITAIN'S HEDGES AND HEDGE TREES

1 *Devon's Hedges.* Devon County Council 1997

2 *Hedgerow Survey Handbook.* Bickmore, C. Countryside Council for Wales 2002

3 *Paper HSG 51 to the Hedgerow Biodiversity Group.* Robertson, R. English Nature 2004

4 *Arbes et biodiversité.* Ministère de L'écologie et du Développement Durable 2002

5 *Article 10, European Council Directive 92/43/EEC of 21 May 1992 on the conservation of natural habitats and of wild flora and fauna*

THE HEDGE TREE POPULATION

1 *Wild Pear.* British Wildlife 11:313-18

2 *Five hundred pointes of good husbandry.* Tusser, T. 1573

3 *The book of husbandry.* Fitzherbert, London 1523

4 *The Gardeners Dictionary Vol III.* Miller, P. London 1741

5 *Hedges and Walls.* Williamson, T. National Trust 2002

6 *Accounting for nature: assessing habitats in the UK countryside.* DETR Publication

7 *Results from MAFF-funded work in the CS2000 Programme.* Barr, C, Stuart, R, Smart, S, and Firbank, L.

'ANCIENT' TREES IN HEDGES

1 *Ancient trees, designation as SSSIs,* Green, T. British Wildlife 12:164-6 2001

2 *The invertebrates of living and decaying timber in Britain and Ireland.* Alexander, K. English Nature Research Reports 2002

3 *Ancient Tree Forum Website.* Alexander, K. 2004

HEDGE TREES AND THE LANDSCAPE

1 *Countryside Character: Vols 1- 8.* The Countryside Agency 1999

REGIONAL HEDGE VARIETIES

1 *Locally distinctive hedgerows:* The Countryside Agency 1999

PREHISTORIC HEDGES

1 *Grazing ecology and forest history.* Vera, F. Holland 2000

2 *Association for Portland Archaeology Website 2004*

3 *Cornish Hedge Group Website 2004*

4 *The History of the Countryside.* Rackham, O. Dent 1986

ROMAN HEDGES AND HEDGE TREES

1 *The History of the Countryside.* Rackham, O. Dent 1986

2 *Four books of husbandry.* Googe, B. London

17TH, 18TH AND 19TH CENTURY HEDGES

1 *The History of the Countryside.* Rackham, O. Dent 1986

2 *Hedges and Walls.* Williamson, T. National Trust 2002

3 *The Gardeners Dictionary Vol III:* Miller, P. London 1741

HEDGE TREES THROUGH HISTORY

1 *The History of the Countryside.* Rackham, O. Dent 1986

2 *Report of the Committee on Hedgerow and Farm Timber.* HMSO 1955

HEDGE TREE AND HEDGE MANAGEMENT

1 *The History of the Countryside.* Rackham, O. Dent 1986

2 *Hedges.* Pollard, E., Hooper, M., and Moore, N. New Naturalist, Collins. 1974

3 *Hedges for farm and garden.* Beddall J. Faber 1950

HEDGE LAYING

1 Adapted from: *Devon's Hedges.* Devon County Council 1997

ESTABLISHING NEW HEDGE TREES

1 *The establishment of trees in hedgerows.* Hodge, S. Forestry Commission Research Information Note 195 1990

CREATING THE ANCIENT TREES OF THE FUTURE

1 *'Veteran Trees: A guide to good management'.* English Nature 2000